Everyday Mathematics®

Student Math Journal 1

The University of Chicago
School Mathematics Project

A Division of The McGraw·Hill Companies

Columbus, Ohio
Chicago, Illinois

UCSMP Elementary Materials Component
Max Bell, Director

Authors

Max Bell
John Bretzlauf
Amy Dillard
Robert Hartfield
Andy Isaacs

James McBride, Director
Kathleen Pitvorec
Peter Saecker
Robert Balfanz*
William Carroll*

Technical Art
Diana Barrie

First Edition only

Photo Credits
Phil Martin/Photography
Page 98: Gus Schalkham, UPI-Bettman
Page 104: Nimatallah/Art Resource, NY

Acknowledgments
Page 157: "Hot Dogs" © 1993 by Consumers Union of U.S., Inc. Yonkers, NY 10703–1057, a nonprofit organization. Reprinted with permission from the August/September 1993 issue of *Zillions* for educational purposes only. http://www.ConsumerReports.org

Page 158: *Science and Engineering Indicators–1998* (DIANE Publishing Company, 1998)

 This material is based upon work supported by the National Science Foundation under Grant No. ESI-9252984. Any opinions, findings, and conclusions or recommendations expressed in this material are those of the authors and do not necessarily reflect the views of the National Science Foundation.

www.sra4kids.com

SRA/McGraw-Hill
A Division of The McGraw-Hill Companies

Send all inquiries to:
SRA/McGraw-Hill
P.O. BOX 812960
Chicago, IL 60681

Printed in the United States of America.

ISBN 1-57039-922-0

11 12 13 14 15 DBH 07 06 05

Contents

Unit 1: Collection, Display, and Interpretation of Data

A note at the bottom of each journal page indicates when that page is first used.
Some pages will be used again during the course of the year.

Unit 2: Operations with Whole Numbers and Decimals

Unit 3: Variables, Formulas, and Graphs

Unit 4: Rational Number Uses and Operations

Unit 5: Geometry: Congruence, Constructions, and Parallel Lines

References

Activity Sheets

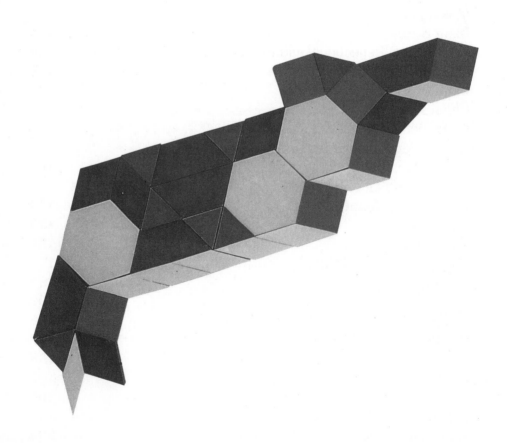

Welcome to *Sixth Grade Everyday Mathematics*

Much of what you learned in the first years of *Everyday Mathematics* served as basic training in mathematics and its uses. In fourth and fifth grades, you built on this training and studied more sophisticated mathematics. This year, you will study new ideas in mathematics—some of which your parents and older siblings may not have learned until high school. The authors, along with many other people, believe that sixth graders today can learn and do more mathematics than was thought possible ten or twenty years ago.

Here are some things you will do in *Sixth Grade Everyday Mathematics:*

- Practice and improve your number sense, measure sense, and estimation skills.

- Review and extend your arithmetic, calculator, and thinking skills by working with fractions, decimals, percents, large and small numbers, and negative numbers.

- Continue your study of variables, expressions, equations, and other topics in algebra.

- Expand your understanding of geometry, with a focus on compass-and-straightedge constructions, transformations of figures, and volumes of 3-dimensional figures.

- Explore probability and statistics.

- Carry out projects that investigate the uses of mathematics outside the classroom.

A *Student Reference Book* is included in the *Sixth Grade Everyday Mathematics* program. This resource book allows you to look up and review information on topics covered in mathematics both this year and in years past. The *Student Reference Book* also includes the rules of popular mathematical games; a glossary of mathematical terms; and reference information, such as tables of measures, fraction-decimal-percent conversion tables, and place-value charts. (Some of this information also appears at the back of your journal.)

This year's activities will help you appreciate the beauty and usefulness of mathematics. The authors hope you will enjoy *Sixth Grade Everyday Mathematics.* Most importantly, we want you to become more skilled at using mathematics so that you may better understand the world in which you live.

Student Reference Book Scavenger Hunt

Solve the problems on this page and on the next two pages. Use your *Student Reference Book* to help you.

Record where you found information in the *Student Reference Book* for each problem. You may not *need* to look for help in the *Student Reference Book,* but you will earn additional points for showing where you *would* look if you needed to.

When the class goes over the answers, keep score as follows:

	Problem Points	**Page Points**

• Give yourself 3 points for each correct answer to a problem.

• Give yourself 5 points for each correct page number in the *Student Reference Book.*

1. Circle the prime numbers: _____ _____

   1   2   6   9   13   20   31   63   72

    Student Reference Book, page _____

2. Circle the composite numbers: _____ _____

   1   2   6   9   13   20   31   63   72

    Student Reference Book, page _____

3. a. 5 meters = _____ centimeters   _____ _____

   b. 300 mm = _____ cm   _____ _____

    *Student Reference Book,* page _____

4. What is the perimeter of this figure? _____   _____ _____

   ```
        ┌──────────────┐
   4 ft │              │
        └──────────────┘
            7 ft
   ```

    Student Reference Book, page _____

Student Reference Book Scavenger Hunt (cont.)

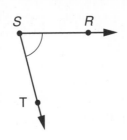

	Problem Points	Page Points

5. Is angle *RST* acute or obtuse? _____
How can you tell?

_____   _____   _____

 Student Reference Book, page _____

6. 3 tablespoons = _____ teaspoons   _____   _____

 Student Reference Book, page _____

7. Rosie had the following scores on her spelling   _____   _____
tests last month: 95, 87, 100, 92, and 78.
What is the mean (or average) of these scores? _____

 Student Reference Book, page _____

8. 23 * 37 = _____   _____   _____

 Student Reference Book, page _____

9. 369 + 1,347 = _____

 Student Reference Book, page _____   _____   _____

10. Is 73,491 divisible by 3? _____   _____   _____

How can you tell without actually dividing?

_____

_____

 Student Reference Book, page _____

11. Add parentheses so that the expression equals 105.   _____   _____

24 − 3 × 5   *Student Reference Book,* page _____

Student Reference Book Scavenger Hunt (cont.)

	Problem Points	Page Points

12. In the number 7.609:   _____   _____

What is the value of the 9? _____

Which digit is in the hundredths place? _____

Student Reference Book, page _____

13. Name two fractions equivalent to $\frac{4}{6}$. _____ and _____   _____   _____

Student Reference Book, page _____

14. What materials do you need to play *Estimation Squeeze?*   _____   _____

_____

Student Reference Book, page _____

15. What is a scalene triangle?   _____   _____

_____

_____

Student Reference Book, page _____

16. Use your calculator to find the square root of 9. _____   _____   _____

Record the key sequence you used.

_____

Total Problem Points	_____
Total Page Points	_____
Total Points	_____

Use with Lesson 1.1.

Math Boxes 1.1

1. Solve.

    a. $4.83 − $2.96 = _____

    b. $5.27 + $6.75 = _____

2. Use your Geometry Template to draw a parallelogram that has all sides the same length.

    This type of parallelogram is also called a

    _____ .

SRB
40 41

SRB
156 157

3. Draw line segments having the following lengths.

    a. $1\frac{1}{4}$ inches

    b. $2\frac{5}{8}$ inches

    c. $\frac{13}{16}$ inch

4. Add.

    a. 2,653 + 4,819 = _____   **b.** 43,708 + 6,493 = _____

    c. _____ = 27 + 109 + 75 + 2,636

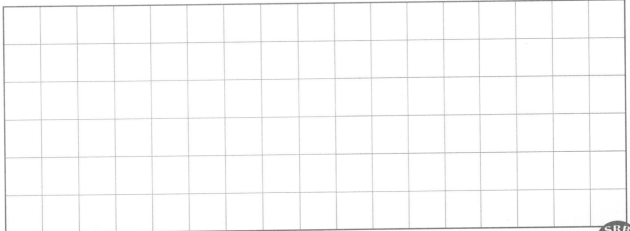

SRB
13 14

Mystery Plots and Landmarks

Math Message

Complete the following statements. *Do not share your answers with anyone.*
Estimate if you do not know the exact number.

A. I usually spend about _____ minutes taking a shower or bath.

B. There is a total of _____ letters in my first, middle, and last names.

C. There are _____ people living in my home.

D. My shoe is about _____ centimeters long (to the nearest cm).

E. I watch about _____ hours of television per week.

Mystery Plots

You and your classmates will make **line plots** of the data from the Math
Message above. You will then try to figure out which line plot, or
"mystery plot," goes with which statement in the Math Message.

Landmarks

After the class has agreed on the subject of each line plot, mark the number lines for
each statement on the next page to show the following **landmarks** of the data or
each statement set: **minimum, maximum, median,** and **mode.** Also record the
range.

Example

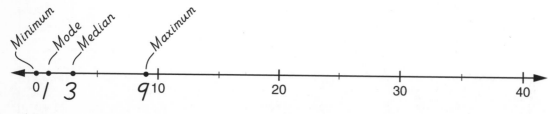

Number of Pets in Home   Range ____9____

Use with Lesson 1.2.

Mystery Plots and Landmarks (cont.)

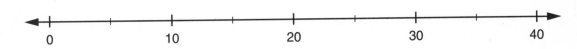

A. Shower/Bath Time (in minutes)   Range _____

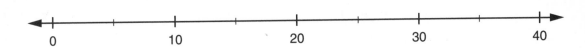

B. Number of Letters in First, Middle, and Last Names   Range _____

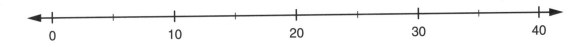

C. Number of People Living in Home   Range _____

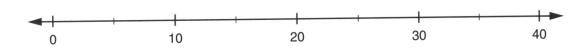

D. Length of Shoe (to nearest cm)   Range _____

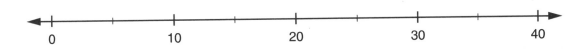

E. Hours of Television Viewed per Week   Range _____

Use with Lesson 1.2.   **7**

Math Boxes 1.2

1. Complete.

    a. 600 * _____ = 54,000

    b. _____ = 80 * 90

    c. 400 * 80 = _____

    d. 560,000 = 700 * _____

    e. 40 * 700 = _____

SRB
18

2. Divide.

    588 ÷ 4 = _____

SRB
22 23

3. Find the perimeter and area of this rectangle.

9 cm

3 cm

perimeter = _____ cm

area = _____ cm²

SRB
194 196

4. Complete.

    a. 3 yd = _____ in.

    b. 6 ft = _____ in.

    c. _____ ft = 24 in.

    d. $3\frac{1}{2}$ ft = _____ in.

    e. _____ yd = 9 ft

    f. 108 in. = _____ ft

SRB
337

5. Subtract.

    a. 900 − 3 = _____   **b.** 5,182 − 2,637 = _____   **c.** _____ = 8,035 − 675

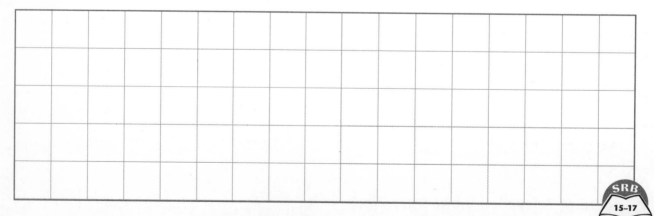
SRB
15–17

Use with Lesson 1.2.

Name-Collection Boxes

Math Message

Every number has many different names. For example, 10 is equal to $8 + 2$; $17 - 7$; $(3 * 5) - 5$; $\frac{1}{2}$ of 20; $\frac{40}{4}$; $6.4 + 3.6$; ten; and so on. In fact, the list is endless.

Write 5 names in each name-collection box. Use as many different kinds of numbers and operations as you can. Label the third box with your own number and then fill in the box.

1.
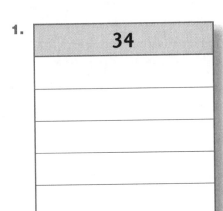

2.

3.

Write 5 names in each name-collection box. Follow the rule for each box.

4. **Rule:** Use as many operations as you want. Use the numbers 3 and 4 in a different way in each expression. Use any other numbers you want.

5. **Rule:** Use as many operations as you want, but use *only* decimals.

15
$(30 / 3) + 4 + 1$

1
$1.5 - 0.5$

Median and Mean

Find the median and mean of each of the following sets of numbers.

1. 123, 56, 92, 90, 88   a. median _____   b. mean _____

2. 0.50, 0.75, 1, 1.25, 0.80   a. median _____   b. mean _____

3. 6, 9, 10, 15   a. median _____   b. mean _____

The 10 most successful coaches in the history of the National Football League are listed at the right, along with the numbers of games won through the end of the 1997-1998 season.

Find the following landmarks for this data set.

4. median   _____

5. maximum   _____

6. minimum   _____

7. mean   _____

8. mode   _____

9. range   _____

Coach	Games Won
Don Shula	347
George Halas	324
Tom Landry	270
Curly Lambeau	229
Chuck Noll	209
Chuck Knox	193
Dan Reeves	172
Paul Brown	170
Bud Grant	168
Steve Owen	155

Source: World Almanac and Book of Facts 2000

10. Alice's first three test scores in math were 90, 100, and 90.

    a. What must Alice score on her fourth test
       to keep her *mean* score at 90 or higher? _____

    b. What must Alice score on her fourth test
       to keep her *median* test score at 90 or higher? _____

    _____

Line Plots and Landmarks

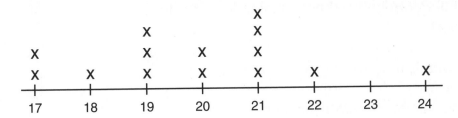

Find the following landmarks for this line plot.

1. maximum _____

2. minimum _____

3. mode _____

4. range _____

5. Weights (in pounds) of emperor penguins:
60, 59, 66, 64, 61, 64, 60, 59, 65, 64, 65, 60

   a. Draw a line plot for the data given above.

   b. Find the following landmarks for this line plot.

      maximum _____

      minimum _____

      mode(s) _____

      range _____

Line Plots and Landmarks (cont.)

6. According to the National Pet Register, the most popular name for a dog in the United States is Jessy.

   a. Which landmark of data is reported by the above statement? _____

   b. How do you think this information was obtained?

   _____

   _____

   _____

7. The Kauai cave wolf spider of the United States is the most endangered spider in the world.

   a. Which landmark of data is reported by the above statement? _____

   b. How do you think this information was obtained?

   _____

   _____

   _____

8. The busiest airport in the world is O'Hare International Airport in Chicago, Illinois. Each year it serves approximately 66,468,000 passengers.

   a. Which landmark of data is reported by the above statement? _____

   b. How do you think this information was obtained?

   _____

   _____

   _____

Source: The Top 10 of Everything

Use with Lesson 1.3.

Math Boxes 1.3

1. Solve.

    a. $7.22 − $3.43 = _____

    b. $9.28 + $2.76 = _____

2. Use your Geometry Template to draw a regular hexagon. Then divide this figure into 6 congruent triangles.

    What kind of triangles are these?

    _____

3. Draw line segments having the following lengths.

    a. $1\frac{3}{4}$ inches

    b. $2\frac{3}{8}$ inches

    c. $\frac{9}{16}$ inch

4. Add.

    a. $4,209 + 6,385 =$ _____   b. $472 + 38,529 =$ _____

    c. _____ $= 4 + 263 + 1,020 + 79$

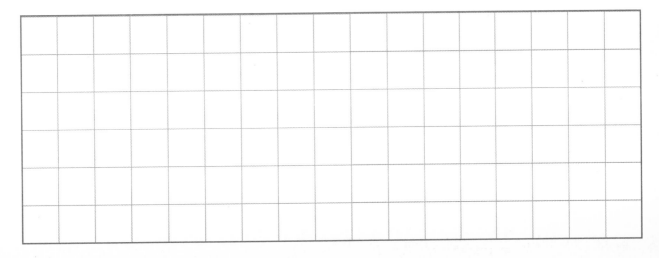

Blast from the Past

Math Message

From *Second Grade Everyday Mathematics:*

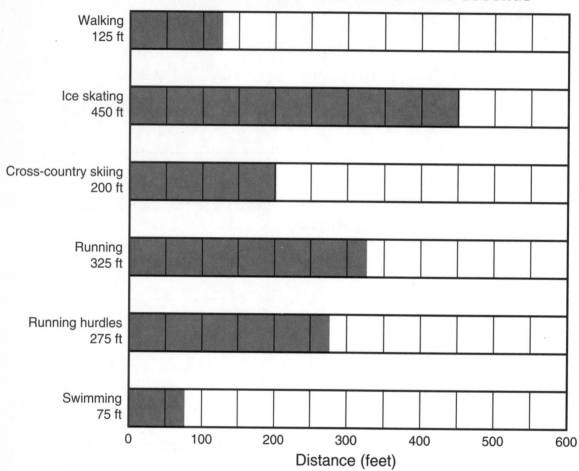

Distances Adults Can Travel in 10 Seconds

Interpret the graph.

1. The longest distance is _____ feet.

2. The shortest distance is _____ feet.

3. The difference between the longest
   distance and the shortest distance (range) is _____ feet.

4. What is a middle value of the distances on the graph? _____ feet

5. About what distance can a cross-country skier cover

   a. in 20 seconds? _____ feet

   b. in 30 seconds? _____ feet

   c. in 1 minute? _____ feet

Math Boxes 1.4

1. Complete.

    a. 800 * _____ = 48,000

    b. _____ = 60 * 40

    c. 1,500 = 50 * _____

    d. 630,000 = 900 * _____

    e. 90 * 300 = _____

2. Divide.

    882 ÷ 7 = _____

3. Find the perimeter and area of this rectangle.

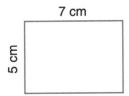

7 cm

5 cm

perimeter = _____ cm

area = _____ cm²

4. Complete.

    a. 42 in. = _____ ft

    b. $3\frac{1}{4}$ ft = _____ in.

    c. _____ in. = 4 yd

    d. $2\frac{1}{2}$ ft = _____ in.

    e. _____ yd = 32 ft

    f. 56 in. = _____ ft

5. Subtract.

    a. 1,000 − 25 = _____   **b.** 2,037 − 294 = _____   **c.** _____ = 7,214 − 6,218

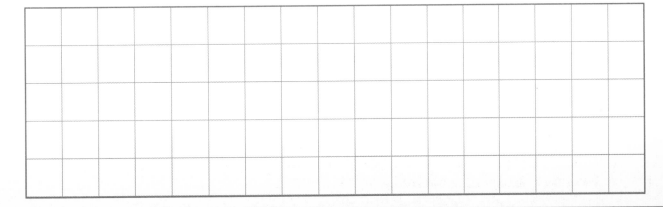

Use with Lesson 1.4.

The Climate in Omaha

Use with Lesson 1.5.

Omaha, the largest city in Nebraska, is located on the eastern border of the state on the Missouri River.

Precipitation is moisture that falls as rain or snow. Rainfall is usually measured in inches; snowfall is usually translated into an equivalent amount of rain.

Average Number of Days in Omaha with at Least 0.01 Inch of Precipitation

Number of days	Jan	Feb	Mar	Apr	May	Jun	Jul	Aug	Sep	Oct	Nov	Dec
	7	6	7	10	12	11	9	9	9	7	5	7

These averages are the result of collecting data over 58 years.

1. Complete the following graph. First make a dot for each month to represent the data in the table. Then connect the dots with line segments. The result is called a **broken-line graph.** This type of graph is often used to show trends.

Average Number of Days in Omaha with at Least 0.01 Inch of Precipitation

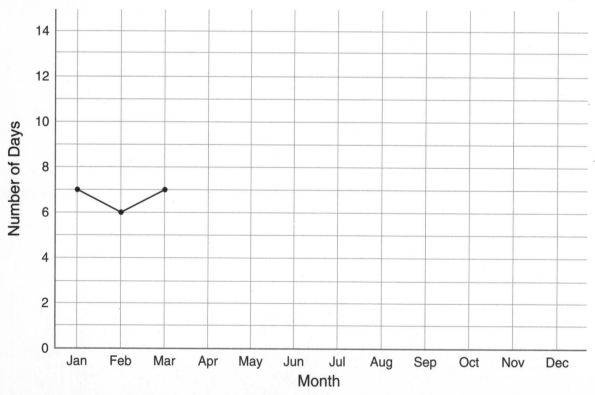

Source: The Times Books World Weather Guide

Use with Lesson 1.5.

The Climate in Omaha (cont.)

Averages of Daily High and Low Temperatures in Omaha, Nebraska

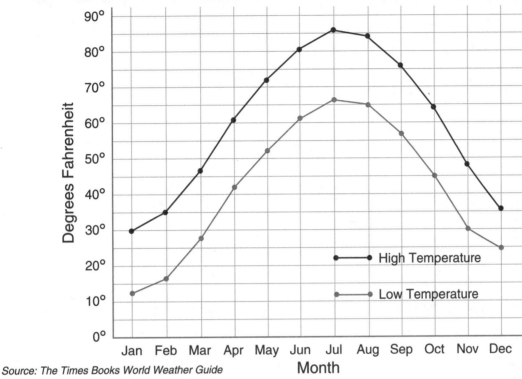

Source: The Times Books World Weather Guide

Here is more information about the climate in Omaha. Black line segments connect the dots for high temperatures. Colored line segments connect low temperatures.

2. On average, what is the

   a. warmest month of the year? _____

   b. the coldest month of the year? _____

3. Compare the average daily high and low temperatures in April. How much warmer is the high temperature? _____

4. Use the graph to fill in the missing data in the following table.

Month	Average daily high temperature	Month	Average daily low temperature
January		April	
November			45°F
	76°F		62°F
	61°F	March	

Math Boxes 1.5

---

1. Complete.

   a. 1,500 / 5 = _____

   b. 8,100 / _____ = 9

   c. _____ / 90 = 50

   d. 28,000 / 70 = _____

   e. _____ = 2,100 / 3

    SRB 21

2. The perimeter of a regular pentagon is 30 feet. What is the length of each side of the pentagon?

   Length of side = _____

    SRB 194 152 153

---

3. a. Is the tub draining or filling?

   _____

   b. What was the height of the water after 3 minutes?

   _____

   Height of Bath Water

   SRB 134

4. Write five names for 1.

   Rule: Use the numbers 5 and 9 in each expression. Use any other numbers you want.

1

    SRB 223

---

5. Thirty students recorded the number of hours they spent watching television during one week. The line plot shows their data.

   Hours Spent Watching Television

   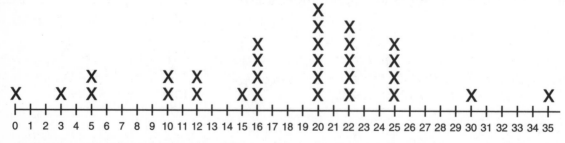

   Find the following landmarks.

   a. maximum _____   b. minimum _____   c. range _____

   d. median _____   e. mode _____

    SRB 128

Drawing and Reading Bar Graphs

1. Mr. Barr gave his class of 25 students a quiz with 5 questions on it.

   • Every student answered at least 2 questions correctly.

   • Three students answered all 5 questions correctly.

   • Ten students answered 4 questions correctly.

   • The same number of students who answered 2 questions correctly answered 3 questions correctly.

   Draw a bar graph to show all of this information. Title the graph and label each axis.

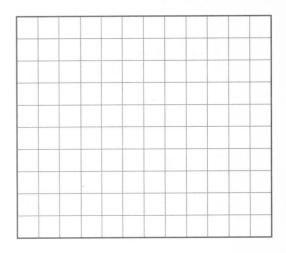

Answer the following questions about the bar graph to the right.

2. Which ski area had the highest snowfall in January 1996? _____

3. About how many inches of snow did Keystone receive in January 1996? _____

4. What is the average January snowfall in Loveland? _____

5. How do the average January snowfalls at Loveland and Arapahoe Basin compare? _____

6. In January 1996, Loveland received how many more inches of snow than Arapahoe Basin? _____

7. Which ski area received the least amount of snow during January 1996? _____

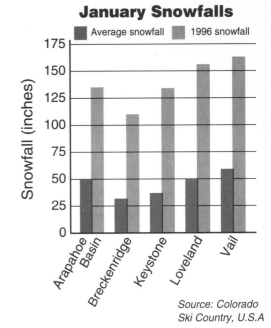

January Snowfalls

Legend: ■ Average snowfall ■ 1996 snowfall

y-axis: Snowfall (inches): 0, 25, 50, 75, 100, 125, 150, 175

x-axis: Arapahoe Basin, Breckenridge, Keystone, Loveland, Vail

Source: Colorado Ski Country, U.S.A

Side-by-Side and Stacked Bar Graphs

Weather in Some Cities in the United States

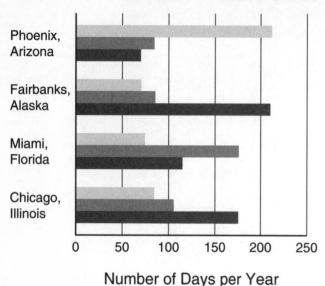

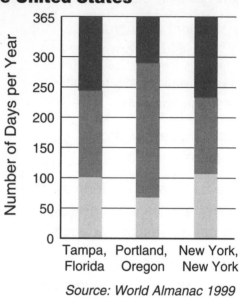

Number of Days per Year

Source: World Almanac 1999

Clear   Partly Cloudy   Cloudy

Use the side-by-side graph to answer Problems 1–3. Use the stacked bar graph to answer Problems 4–6. Circle the correct answers.

1. About how many cloudy days does Fairbanks have yearly?

   a. 70

   b. 85

   c. 210

2. Which city ranks second in the number of clear days per year?

   a. Chicago

   b. Miami

   c. Phoenix

3. Which of these pairs of cities have the most similar weather?

   a. Phoenix and Fairbanks

   b. Fairbanks and Chicago

   c. Miami and Chicago

4. About how many clear days does Portland have yearly?

   a. 50

   b. 70

   c. 100

5. Which city has the greatest number of partly cloudy days?

   a. Portland

   b. Tampa

   c. New York

6. About how many cloudy days does New York have yearly?

   a. 110

   b. 130

   c. 230

                                                Use with Lesson 1.6.

Temperatures above Earth's Surface

When you fly in a commercial airplane, you probably don't notice any large changes in temperature, because the cabin is temperature controlled. But if you are riding in a hot-air balloon, you feel the temperature drop as the balloon rises.

The table below shows temperatures at various heights above Omaha, Nebraska. The measurements were made on a January day when the temperature at ground level was 32°F. Reminder: 1 mile = 5,280 feet.

Height above Ground (miles)	Temperature (°F)
0 (ground level)	32°
1	25°
2	15°
3	−5°
4	−25°
4.5	−40°
5.5	−60°
10	−75°

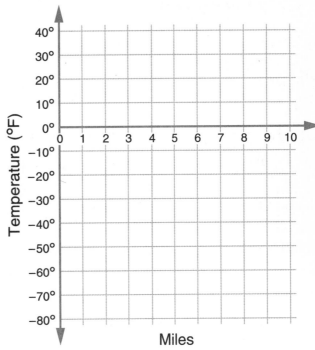

Temperature above Ground Level

1. Make a broken-line graph of the data in the table.

2. At about what height above the ground was the temperature 0°F? _____

3. What was the approximate temperature 8 miles above Omaha? _____

4. Suppose an airplane was about 26,000 feet above Omaha on the day recorded in the table.

   a. What was the approximate temperature at 26,000 feet? _____

   b. How much colder was the temperature at 26,000 feet above ground than at ground level? _____

Math Boxes 1.6

1. Multiply.

   a. $57 * 34 =$ _____

   b. _____ $= 308 * 78$

SRB
19 20

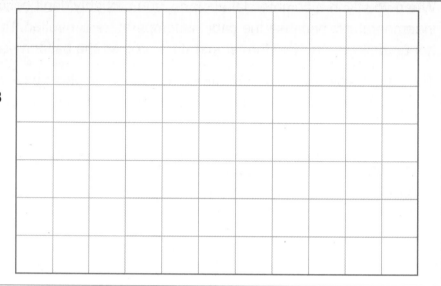

2. Use the following bar graph to answer the questions below.

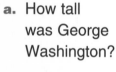

   a. How tall was George Washington?

   _____

   b. How tall was Zachary Taylor?

   _____

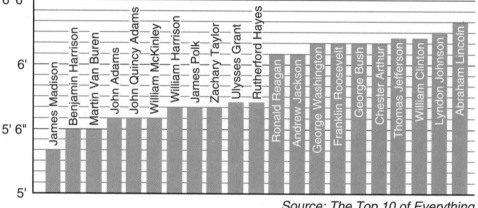

Heights of the Shortest and Tallest U.S. Presidents

Source: The Top 10 of Everything

   c. Who was the shortest president? _____

   d. Who was the tallest president? _____

   e. What was the difference in height between the tallest and shortest presidents? _____

   f. Which height occurs most often for the presidents listed? _____

   g. What was the difference in height between Ulysses Grant and Chester Arthur? _____

SRB
132

The Cost of Mailing a Letter

The graph below is called a **step graph.** It shows the cost of sending a letter weighing 1 ounce or less by first-class mail anywhere in the United States.

Cost of Mailing a First-Class Letter Anywhere in the U.S. 1900—2000

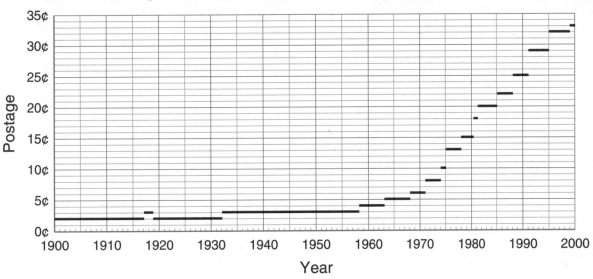

1. The cost of mailing a letter was 3 cents from 1932 until _____.

2. Did the cost of mailing a letter ever go down? If so, when? _____

3. How many rate increases were there between 1960 and 1970? _____

4. In which year did the *greatest* increase occur? _____

5. By how much did the cost of mailing a letter increase between 1960 and 1970? _____

6. Can you tell from the graph the cost of mailing a letter before 1900? _____

7. In which year do you think the cost of mailing a letter will reach 50 cents? Explain.

_____

_____

_____

_____

_____

Taxicab Fares

The A-1 Taxicab Company charges for a ride according to the distance covered.
Here is the company's table of fares.

Distance	Fare
More than 0 miles, not more than 1 mile	$2.00
More than 1 mile, not more than 2 miles	$4.00
More than 2 miles, not more than 3 miles	$5.00
More than 3 miles, not more than 4 miles	$6.00
More than 4 miles, not more than 5 miles	$7.00
More than 5 miles, not more than 6 miles	$8.00
More than 6 miles, not more than 7 miles	$9.00
More than 7 miles, not more than 8 miles	$10.00

1. Use the data in the table to complete
   the step graph at the right.

2. What is the cost of the fare
   for each distance below?

   a. 3.7 miles _____

   b. 7.1 miles _____

   c. 0.1 mile _____

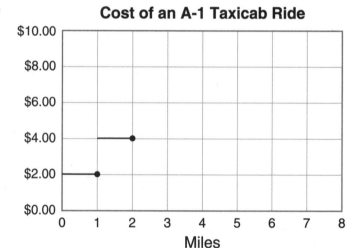

Cost of an A-1 Taxicab Ride

3. You have $7.50. What is
   the longest trip you can take? _____ miles

4. Your ride cost $5.00.

   a. What is the shortest trip you could have taken? _____ miles

   b. What is the longest trip you could have taken? _____ miles

A Plumber's Rates

The step graph below shows the cost of hiring a Drain-Right plumber for various amounts of time.

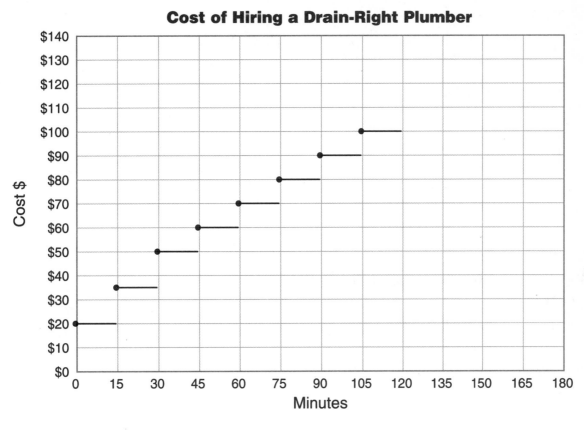

Cost of Hiring a Drain-Right Plumber

1. A Drain-Right plumber charged $80.00 for doing a job.

   a. What is the shortest time the job could have taken? _____ minutes

   b. What is the longest time the job could have taken? _____ minutes

2. Use the graph to fill in the table below.

Time (minutes)	20	59	12	120	60	96
Cost						

3. Notice the pattern of the step graph between 45 and 120 minutes. Use this pattern to complete the step graph for all times between 120 and 180 minutes.

Date _____ Time _____

Math Boxes 1.7

1. Complete.

   a. 1,800 / 6 = _____

   b. 6,400 / _____ = 8

   c. _____ / 50 = 50

   d. 42,000 / 60 = _____

   e. _____ = 3,600 / 4

2. Find the perimeter of a regular hexagon whose sides are 9 centimeters long.

   perimeter = _____ cm

3. a. What was the height at 5 weeks?

   _____ in.

   b. How many inches did the plant grow between Weeks 3 and 4?

   _____ in.

Height of Bean Plant

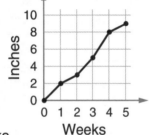

4. Write five names for 24.

   Rule: Use *only* the numbers 2 and 6 in each expression.

5. The line plot below shows the first-place times in the men's 100-meter run at the Olympic Games from 1896 to 1992. Times are rounded to tenths of a second. Find the following landmarks (to tenths of a second) for the data set.

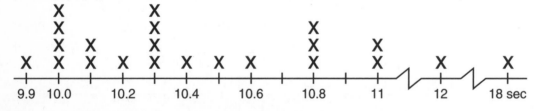

Source: World Almanac and Book of Facts 1996

   a. maximum _____   **b.** minimum _____   **c.** range _____

   d. median _____   **e.** mode(s) _____

26   Use with Lesson 1.7.

Math Boxes 1.8

---

1. Multiply.

    a. $81 * 13 =$ _____

    b. _____ $= 243 * 72$

---

2. Use the bar graph to answer the questions below.

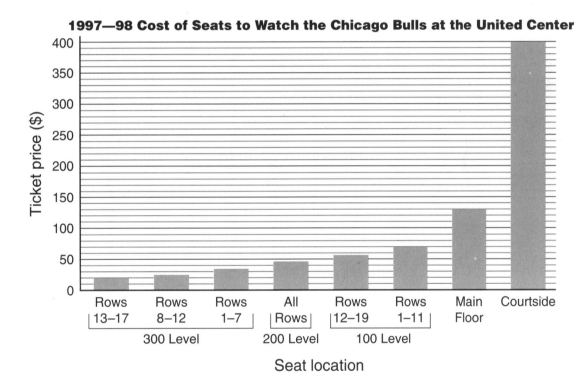

    a. How much do the cheapest seats at the United Center cost? _____

    b. What is the range of prices for seats? _____

    c. What is the median price of a 300-level seat? _____

    d. Mr. Harris wants to buy four 100-level seats. How much would he save if he bought the cheaper 100-level seats rather than the more expensive 100-level seats?

    _____

A Magazine Survey

The December 1995 issue of a sports magazine for kids featured a readers' survey.
The circle graphs below show readers' responses to three questions.
Give your response to each question.

Question: On how many organized sports
teams do you play during a year? _____

Readers' Responses

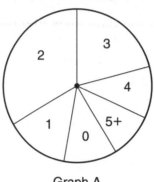

Graph A

Question: Should girls be allowed to play on boys' teams? _____

Readers' Responses

Girls say:

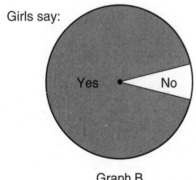

Graph B

Boys say:

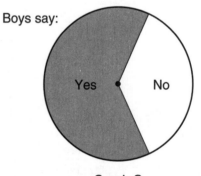

Graph C

Question: Should boys be allowed to play on girls' teams? _____

Readers' Responses

Girls say:

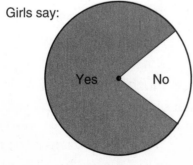

Graph D

Boys say:

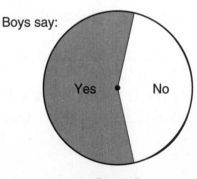

Graph E

Source:
Sports Illustrated for Kids

28

Use with Lesson 1.8.

A Magazine Survey (cont.)

Refer to the circle graphs on the preceding page to answer the following questions.

1. Estimate the percent of boys and girls who gave the following responses.

   a. Approximately _____% play on 2 organized teams during a typical year.

   b. Approximately _____% play on *at least* 2 organized teams during a year.

   c. Approximately _____% of the girls think that girls should *not* be allowed to play on boys' teams.

2. Which graph (B, C, D, or E) shows
   almost everyone agreeing on an answer? _____

3. Which graph (B, C, D, or E) shows opinions
   that are almost evenly divided between yes and no? _____

4. Do you think that the readers of the sports magazine who responded to this survey play sports more often, less often, or about the same amount of time as the students in your school?

   _____

   Explain. _____

   _____

   _____

   _____

5. Summarize how the boys and girls who responded to this survey feel about allowing opposite-gender players on boys' and girls' teams.

   _____

   _____

   _____

   _____

   _____

   _____

Reading Circle Graphs

Use your estimation skills and your Percent Circle to answer the following questions.

1. The circle graph at the right shows people's preferences for preparing eggs.

   Methods of Preparing Eggs

   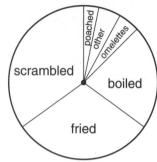

   Source: American Egg Board

   a. Which is the most popular method for preparing eggs? _____

   b. Which is the least popular method for preparing eggs? _____

   c. Which method is preferred by about 25% of the people surveyed? _____

   d. Which methods are preferred by less than 10% of the people surveyed?

   _____

   e. What percent of people surveyed prefer scrambled eggs? About _____%

   f. Is the percent greater for people favoring fried eggs or boiled eggs? _____

      About how much greater? _____%

   g. How do you like your eggs prepared? _____

2. The circle graph at the right shows people's preferences for pizza crust.

   Pizza Crust Preferences

   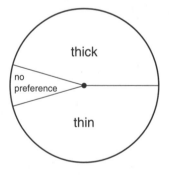

   Source: Pizza Today

   a. True or false: In this survey, the number of people who prefer thin-crust pizza is about the same as the number of people who prefer thick-crust pizza.

      _____

   b. What percent of people prefer thin-crust pizza?   About _____%

   c. What percent prefer thick-crust pizza?   About _____%

   d. What percent have no preference?   About _____%

   e. What kind of crust do you prefer? _____

Use with Lesson 1.8.

1. Write the value of the digit 9 in each numeral below.

a. 401,297 _____

b. 1,927,387 _____

c. 4.95 _____

2. Find the median and mean of each set of numbers.

a. 13, 29, 18, 34, 21

median _____   mean _____

b. 42, 16, 51, 41

median _____   mean _____

3. According to the circle graph at the right:

a. Which kind of peanut butter do most Americans prefer? _____

b. Which kind is preferred by about $\frac{1}{3}$ of Americans? _____

c. About what percent of Americans prefer natural peanut butter? _____

Peanut Butter Survey

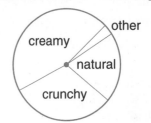

Source: Astounding Averages

4. Make a step graph of the information shown in this table.

Years	1901–1960	1961	1962–1968	1969–1976	1977–1992	1993–1997
Number of Major League Teams	16	18	20	24	26	28

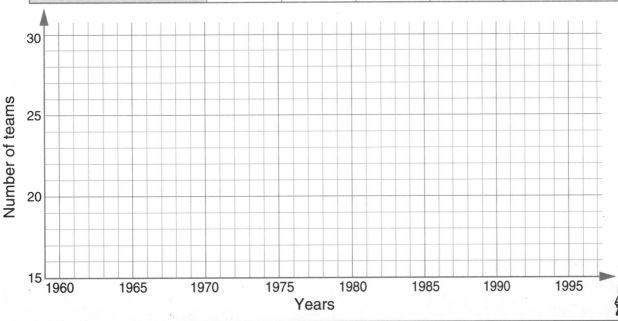

Using a Graph to Find the Largest Area

Math Message

Suppose you have enough material for 22 feet of fence. You want to enclose the largest possible rectangular region with this fence.

1. If you know the perimeter and length of a rectangle, how can you find its width?

    _____

    _____

2. The table below lists the lengths of some rectangles with a perimeter of 22 ft. Fill in the missing widths and areas. If it helps, draw the rectangles on your grid paper. Let the side of each grid square represent 1 foot.

Length (ft)	1	2	3	4	5	6	7	8	9	10
Width (ft)	10	9								
Perimeter (ft)	22	22	22	22	22	22	22	22	22	22
Area (ft²)	10	18					28			

3. If you have not already done so, draw each rectangle from the table above on your grid paper.

4. a. What are the length and width of the rectangle(s) in the table with the largest area? _____

    b. What is that area? _____ ft²

5. On the graph on page 33, plot the length and area of each rectangle in the table. *Do not connect the dots.*

6. a. Find a rectangle whose perimeter is 22 feet and whose area is larger than the area of the rectangle in Problem 4 above. Use your graph to help you.

    What is the length? _____ ft   width? _____ ft   area? _____ ft²

    b. Now plot the length and area of this rectangle on the grid on page 33. Then draw a curved line through all the dots.

Use with Lesson 1.9.

Using a Graph to Find the Largest Area (cont.)

Areas of Rectangles

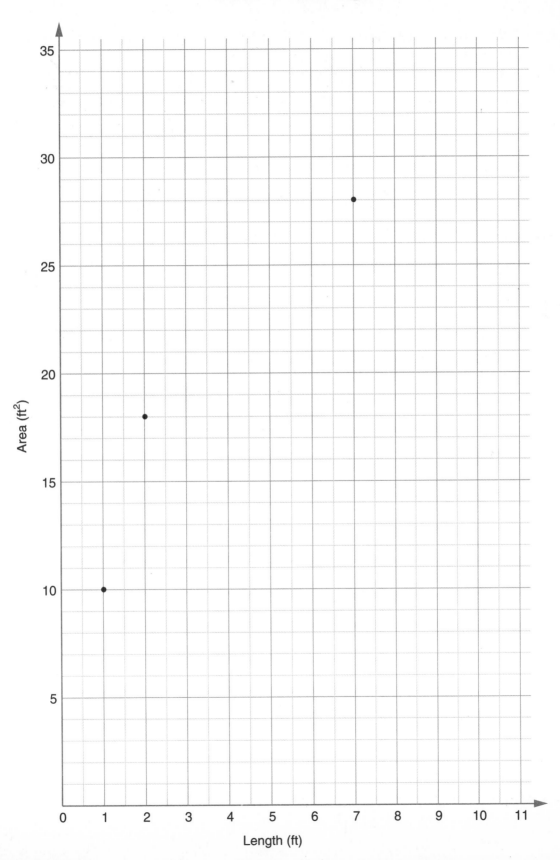

Date _____ Time _____

Statistics Meant to Astound the Reader

Americans Consume 90 Acres of Pizza a Day!
Each day we eat 90 football fields covered with pizza!
The National Association of Pizza Operators reported today that

Ninety acres may seem like a tremendous amount of pizza. The person who wrote this headline wants us to think so. However, let's look at this statistic more closely.

 There are 43,560 square feet in an acre, so 90 acres is about 3,900,000 square feet of pizza.

$90 * 43,560 = 3,920,400$
Round to 3,900,000.

 If Americans eat 3,900,000 square feet of pizza each day for 365 days, that is about 1,420,000,000 square feet of pizza per year.

$3,900,000 * 365 = 1,423,500,000$
Round to 1,420,000,000.

 If 1,420,000,000 square feet of pizza is divided by 270,000,000 people in the United States, then each person, on average, eats about 5 square feet of pizza per year.

$1,420,000,000 / 270,000,000 = 5.\overline{259}$
Round to 5.

Suppose an average pizza is about 1 square foot in area. Then each person in the United States eats approximately 5 pizzas per year.

Here is a new headline based on the information above.

An Average American Eats 5 Pizzas per Year!
The National Association of Pizza Operators reported today that

1. Study this headline.

An Average American Takes about 50,000 Automobile Trips in a Lifetime!

Write a new headline that gives the same information but will not astound the reader.

34

Use with Lesson 1.10.

Date

Time

Analyzing Persuasive Graphs

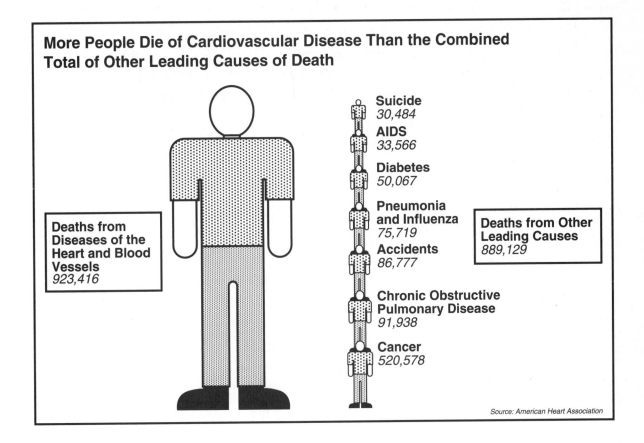

More People Die of Cardiovascular Disease Than the Combined Total of Other Leading Causes of Death

Suicide
30,484

AIDS
33,566

Diabetes
50,067

Pneumonia and Influenza
75,719

Accidents
86,777

Chronic Obstructive Pulmonary Disease
91,938

Cancer
520,578

Deaths from Diseases of the Heart and Blood Vessels
923,416

Deaths from Other Leading Causes
889,129

Source: American Heart Association

1. What is mathematically wrong with the picture above?

_____

_____

_____

_____

_____

_____

_____

_____

_____

_____

_____

Analyzing Persuasive Graphs (cont.)

You are trying to convince your parents that you deserve an increase in your weekly allowance. You claim that over the past 10 weeks, you have spent more time doing jobs around the house, such as emptying the trash, mowing the lawn, and cleaning up after dinner. You have decided to present this information to your parents in the form of a graph. You have made two versions of the graph and need to decide which one to use.

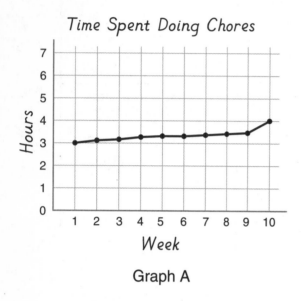

Graph A

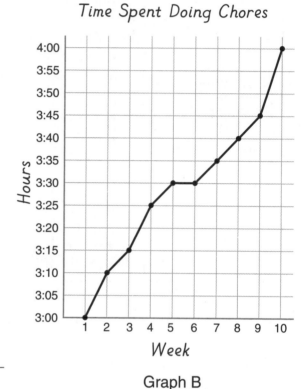

Graph B

2. How are Graph A and Graph B similar?

_____

_____

3. How are Graph A and Graph B different?

_____

_____

4. Which graph, A or B, do you think will help you the most as you try to convince your parents that you deserve a raise in your allowance? Why?

_____

_____

_____

Math Boxes 1.10

1. Multiply.

   a. 53 * 92 = _____

   b. _____ = 371 * 25

2. Use the bar graph to answer the questions below.

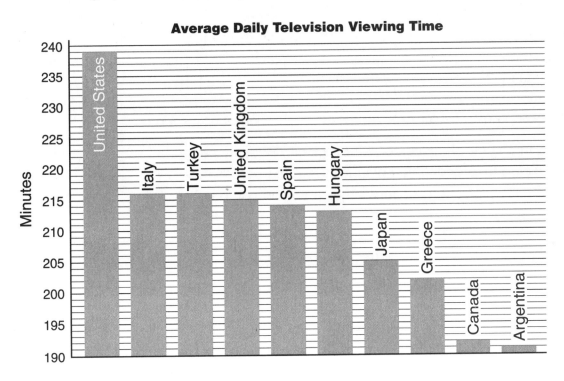

Average Daily Television Viewing Time

   a. On average, how much time do people from Japan spend watching television each day?

   _____ minutes

   b. Which country has the shortest average daily viewing time? _____

   c. Which viewing time occurs most often? _____ minutes

   d. What is the difference in viewing time between Canada and the United Kingdom?

   _____ minutes

Kitchen Units of Capacity

Math Message

Complete the following equivalents.

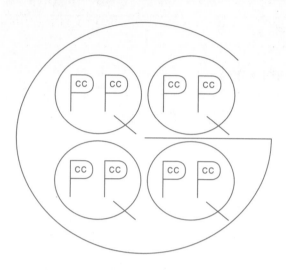

1 pint = _____ cups

1 quart = _____ pints

1 quart = _____ cups

1 gallon = _____ quarts

1 gallon = _____ cups

Be prepared to discuss the following question: How can the picture above help you remember how many cups are in a pint, how many pints are in a quart, and how many quarts are in a gallon?

---

1. **a.** Three gallons of juice will provide _____ one-cup servings.

   b. You are in charge of buying food for a picnic. Seventy people are expected to attend. If you plan to give each person 1 cup of juice, how many gallons of juice should you buy? _____

2. **a.** If you drink 1 cup of milk each day, about how many gallons of milk do you drink per month? _____

   b. About how many gallons of milk per year? _____

3.   1 cup = 8 fl oz   Capacity of 1 soft-drink can: 12 fl oz

   a. How many cups are there in 2 cans of soft drink? _____

   b. About how many cans of soft drink are there per gallon? _____

Challenge

4. Which contains more? Circle the answer.

   a. A 2-quart bottle   or   a 6-pack of 12-oz cans?

   b. A 2-gallon bottle   or   a 24-pack of 12-oz cans?

Date _____ Time _____

Drinking Habits of Children and Teenagers

Read the newspaper article below. Then complete the table and answer the questions.

What kids are drinking

For years, experts lauded milk's nutritional value, but now they are questioning its role in the diet of children who suffer from allergies and sinus and intestinal problems. Children are drinking less milk, but the popularity of juices and soft drinks is increasing.

Sources: U.S. Dept. of Agriculture; Chicago Tribune

► **What children drink**
Average amounts consumed by 6- to 11-year-olds per year:

Milk
1978 46.4 gal
1994 38.7 gal

Apple and grape juices
1978 1.4 gallons
1994 3.5 gallons

Soft drinks
1978 10.6 gallons
1994 20.0 gallons

► **What teenagers drink**
Average amounts consumed by 12- to 19-year-olds per year:

Milk
1978 49.6 gal
1994 32.9 gal

Apple and grape juices
1978 0.8 gallons
1994 2.7 gallons

Soft drinks
1978 20.6 gallons
1994 62.5 gallons

	6- to 11-year-olds	12- to 19-year-olds
Most popular drink in 1978		
Most popular drink in 1994		
Gallons of soft drinks in 1994		

1. In 1994, 12- to 19-year-olds drank an average of how many gallons of milk per year? _____

2. Are apple and grape juices more or less popular now than they were 20 years ago? _____

3. True or false?

   _____ a. Today, teenagers drink about 3 times as many soft drinks as they did 20 years ago.

   _____ b. In 1978 and 1994, teenagers drank more gallons of soft drinks than milk.

   _____ c. In 1994, both children and teens drank about 1 gallon of milk per week.

Challenge

4. If you drank 62.5 gallons of soft drinks, how many 12-ounce cans would that be? About _____ cans

Use with Lesson 1.11.

39

Circle Graphs, Median, and Mean

1. The circle graph below shows the approximate percent of the world's population on each continent. Use the Percent Circle on your Geometry Template to answer the following questions.

   a. Which continent contains more than half of the world's population? _____

   b. About what percent of the world's population lives in North America? _____

   c. Do more people live in Europe or in Africa? _____

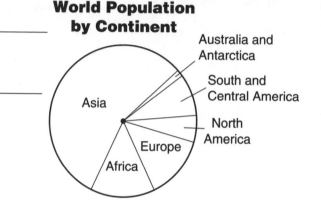

World Population by Continent

   d. The population of the world is approximately 5.5 billion people. Circle the best estimate for the number of people in Asia.

   3 million   30 million   300 million   3 billion

2. The statements below may or may not be true. Circle the letter of each statement that you can determine is true based on the graph in Problem 1.

   a. The population of South and Central America is nearly double the population of North America.

   b. In Asia, the population is increasing faster than on any other continent.

   c. There are more people in the United States than in Germany.

   d. The number of people in Europe is about equal to the total number of people in North, South, and Central America.

3. Elaine tried the long jump 5 times. Her distances were 56 inches, 62 inches, 34 inches, 58 inches, and 62 inches.

   a. What is the median of Elaine's long jumps? _____

   b. What is the mean? _____

   c. Which landmark do you think best represents Elaine's typical jump? _____

Use with Lesson 1.11.

Date _____ Time _____

Math Boxes 1.11

1. Write the value of the digit 3 in each numeral below.

a. 456,396 _____

b. 3,598,902 _____

c. 8.43 _____

2. Find the median and mean of each set of numbers below.

a. 7, 2, 12, 5, 9, 18

median _____ mean _____

b. 21, 47, 34, 96, 71

median _____ mean _____

3. Use these circle graphs to answer the following questions.

a. About what percent of the content of bread is water?

_____

b. About what percent of the content of a ripe tomato is water?

_____

Percent of Water in Foods

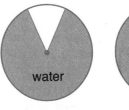

bread   pineapple   ripe tomato

Source: Astounding Averages

4. From 1860 to 1861, eleven states seceded from the United States. All eleven states were reinstated between 1866 and 1870. (Four new states joined the Union between 1860 and 1866.) The table at the left shows the number of states in the United States from 1859 to 1870. Make a step graph to display this information.

Years	Number of States in the U.S.
1859	33
1860	32
1861-1862	23
1863	24
1864-1865	25
1866	26
1867	27
1868-1869	34
1870	37

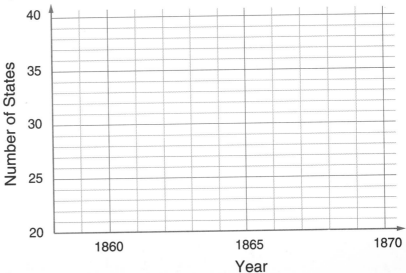

Use with Lesson 1.11.

41

Time to Reflect

1. What was something especially interesting that you learned in this unit?

   _____

   _____

   _____

   _____

2. What questions do you still have about the material covered in this unit?

   _____

   _____

   _____

   _____

3. How would one low test score affect the mean of 4 high test scores?
   Give an example.

   _____

   _____

   _____

   _____

   _____

4. Describe a situation in which it is important to know the mode of a set of data.

   _____

   _____

   _____

   _____

   _____

Use with Lesson 1.12.

Math Boxes 1.12

---

1. Solve.

   a. $7.25 − $3.87 = _____

   b. $6.58 + $8.62 = _____

---

2. Complete.

   a. 400 * _____ = 20,000

   b. _____ = 40 * 90

   c. 150 = 30 * _____

   d. 720,000 = 800 * _____

   e. 60 * 700 = _____

---

3. Complete.

   a. 4,500 / 5 = _____

   b. 3,600 / _____ = 6

   c. _____ / 80 = 30

   d. 48,000 / 60 = _____

   e. _____ = 4,900 / 7

---

4. Write the value of the digit 7 in each numeral below.

   a. 7,856,346 _____

   b. 2,796,002 _____

   c. 0.937 _____

   d. 6.7 _____

---

5. Divide.

   768 ÷ 6 = _____

---

6. Multiply.

   45 * 97 = _____

Adding and Subtracting Decimals

Math Message

Solve.

1. $\begin{array}{r} 32.5 \\ +\ 19.6 \\ \hline \end{array}$

2. $\begin{array}{r} 5.67 \\ -\ 1.84 \\ \hline \end{array}$

Solve.

3. $\begin{array}{r} 4.07 \\ +\ 9.38 \\ \hline \end{array}$

4. $\begin{array}{r} 0.671 \\ +\ 8.935 \\ \hline \end{array}$

5. $\begin{array}{r} 4.3 \\ 3.9 \\ 7.2 \\ 8.1 \\ 14.6 \\ +\ 2.5 \\ \hline \end{array}$

6. $\begin{array}{r} 49.2 \\ -\ 27.6 \\ \hline \end{array}$

7. $\begin{array}{r} 5.006 \\ -\ 0.392 \\ \hline \end{array}$

8. $\begin{array}{r} 7.03 \\ -\ 4.96 \\ \hline \end{array}$

           Use with Lesson 2.1.

Adding and Subtracting Decimals (cont.)

9. In the 1968 Olympic Games, the United States women's 400-meter medley relay
   team won this swimming event with a time of 4 minutes, 28.3 seconds. In 1972,
   the United States women's team won again in 4 minutes, 20.75 seconds. How
   much faster was the 1972 team than the 1968 team?

   _____
                                    (unit)

10. In the 1924 Olympic Games, Fred Tootell of the United States won the hammer
    throw with a distance of 53.295 meters. In 1928, Patrick O'Callaghan of Ireland
    won with a distance of 51.39 meters.

    a. Which man threw the greater distance? _____

    b. By how much? _____

11. 15.327 + 6.09 = _____

12. 9.4 − 3.605 =   _____

13. 3.7 + 13.589 =   _____

14. 0.8 − 0.045 =   _____

15. The perimeter of
    the rectangle below is _____.
                                              (unit)

    85 cm ┌─────────────┐
           │   │
           └─────────────┘
             2.6 m

16. One container holds 3.8 liters of liquid. Another
    container holds 500 milliliters of liquid. How much
    do the two containers hold in all?

    _____
                                    (unit)

Math Boxes 2.1

1. Plot and label the following points on the coordinate grid.

   A: (4,5)

   B: (−3,6)

   C: (2,−2)

   D: (0,4)

   E: (−6,−3)

   F: (1,0)

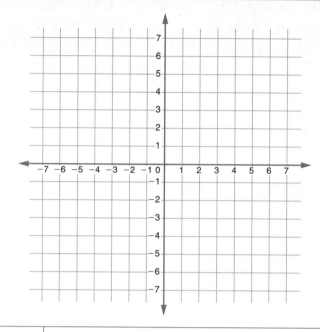

216

2. The school supply store purchased 500 notebooks. They were shipped in boxes that could hold 12 notebooks each. How many boxes were needed to ship the entire order?

   _____

   239

3. Complete.

   a. 21 c = _____ pt _____ c

   b. 54 qt = _____ gal _____ qt

   c. 4 qt = _____ pt

   d. 9 gal 2 qt = _____ qt

   337

4. Measure each line segment to the nearest tenth of a centimeter.

   a. ————————————————————

   _____ cm

   b. ————————————————————————

   _____ cm

   c. ——————————————

   _____ cm

Use with Lesson 2.1.

Multiplying Decimals

Math Message

1. Toni has a set of metal discs. Each disc has a thickness
   of 0.3 cm. If she puts 8 of the discs in a stack, what will
   be the height of the stack?   _____

2. a. Estimate the product of 2.1 * 3.4.   About _____

   b. Find the exact answer to 21 * 34. Use your estimate
      to place the decimal point correctly in the product of 2.1 * 3.4.   _____

3. This June, 1.4 inches of rain fell in Carrollville.
   The average rainfall for the month is 4 times as much.
   What is the average rainfall for June?   _____

4. Stamps cost $0.33 each. How much will 25 stamps cost?   _____

5. Find the area of each rectangle below.

   a.   30 cm
      1.5 cm [   ]   area = _____ cm²

   b.   3.5 cm
      1.8 cm [   ]   area = _____ cm²

6. Joe buys the *Morning Star* newspaper each day. The price of the paper
   is 35 cents a day on Monday through Saturday. The Sunday edition
   costs $1.75. How much does Joe spend in a week on the newspaper?   _____

7. Tina multiplied correctly but forgot to place the decimal point in the product below.

   a. Place it correctly for her.   12.3 * 5.07 = 6 2 3 6 1

   b. Explain how you knew where to place the decimal.

      _____

      _____

      _____

Multiplying Decimals (cont.)

For each of the problems below, the multiplication has been done, but the decimal point has not been placed in the product. Place it correctly.

8. $2.3 * 7.3 = $ 1 6 7 9

9. $51 * 3.8 = $ 1 9 3 8

10. $6.91 * 8.2 = $ 5 6 6 6 2

11. $0.2 * 5.777 = $ 1 1 5 5 4

12. Explain how you decided where to place the decimal point for Problem 11.

_____

_____

13. Jawanda used her calculator to multiply $9.1 * 2.3$. She got the answer 209.3.

   a. Explain why this is not a reasonable answer.

_____

_____

   b. What do you think Jawanda might have done wrong?

_____

_____

Without using a calculator, find each of the following products. Use estimation to help you place each decimal point.

14. $2.7 * 4.5 = $ _____

15. $24 * 5.1 = $ _____

16. $0.2 * 5.4 = $ _____

Use with Lesson 2.2.

Date _____ Time _____

Math Boxes 2.2

1. On average, Americans use about 27 gallons of water to shower.

   a. That's about how many half-gallons? _____

   b. About how many quarts? _____

   c. If a person took 1 shower a day, about how many gallons would the person use in 1 year? Circle the best estimate.

   10   1,000   10,000   100,000

SRB 337

2. Write each number in standard notation.

   a. $7^2 =$ _____

   b. $5^3 =$ _____

   c. $2^5 =$ _____

   d. $3^4 =$ _____

   e. $10^6 =$ _____

SRB 6

3. Write five names for 3.6. *Rule:* You must use addition or multiplication in each expression.

3.6

SRB 223

4. Divide.

596 / 12 → _____

SRB 22–24

5. Add or subtract.

  a. 23.6   **b.** 108.63   **c.** 0.439   **d.** $7 - 3.14 =$ _____
     + 5.4   − 96.17   + 0.04

SRB 38–41

More Multiplying Decimals

Math Message

Use the lattice method to solve the problems.

1. 28 * 13 = _____

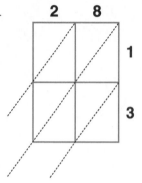

2. 2.8 * 1.3 = _____

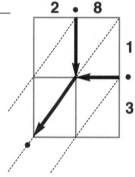

Use the product of 456 and 78 to solve the following problems.

3. 45.6 * 7.8   =   _____

4. 456 * 0.78   =   _____

5. 4.56 * 78   =   _____

6. 0.456 * 7.8   =   _____

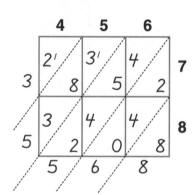

Use with Lesson 2.3.

More Multiplying Decimals (cont.)

Use any multiplication algorithm you wish to solve the following problems.

7.   3.4
   * 7.9

8.   0.46
   * 0.83

9.   19.6
   *   4

10.   23.65
    *   8

11.   0.48
    * 25.4

12.   0.21
    *   26

13.   4.8
    * 15

14.   1.52
    *   0.3

Solve the following problems mentally.

15. 1.5 * 10 = _____

16. 0.25 * 6 = _____

17. _____ = 1.2 * 0.5

18. 0.03 * 6.2 = _____

19. 5.1 * 0.4 = _____

20. _____ = 0.07 * 0.6

21. _____ = 3.42 * 0.2

22. _____ = 4 * 9.1

Use with Lesson 2.3.   **51**

The Cost of a Telephone Call

The cost of a telephone call usually depends on how long the call lasts.
Here is how one phone company charges for calls.

Length of Call	Cost
more than **0** minutes, but not more than **20** minutes	$1.00
more than **20** minutes, but not more than **21** minutes	$1.10
more than **21** minutes, but not more than **22** minutes	$1.20
more than **22** minutes, but not more than **23** minutes	$1.30
more than **23** minutes, but not more than **24** minutes	$1.40

1. Use the data in the table to complete the step graph below.

Give the cost for each phone call.

2. 1 minute costs

   $_____.

3. 12 minutes cost

   $_____.

4. 20 minutes cost

   $ _____.

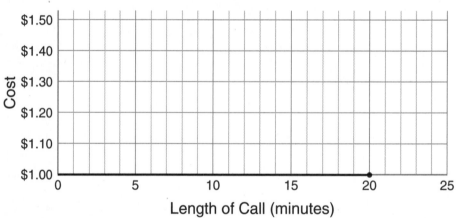

Cost of Phone Calls

5. 22 minutes and 38 seconds cost $ _____.

6. A phone call costs $1.40.

   a. What is the *shortest* amount of time that the phone call could have lasted?

   _____

   b. What is the *longest* amount of time that the phone call could have lasted?

   _____

Math Boxes 2.3

1. Write the number pair for each of the following points shown on the coordinate grid.

A: (_____,_____)

B: (_____,_____)

C: (_____,_____)

D: (_____,_____)

E: (_____,_____)

F: (_____,_____)

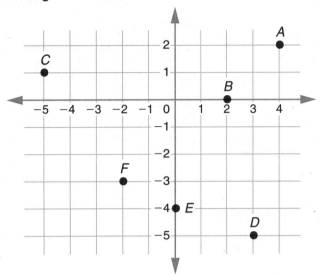

2. Seventy-seven children signed up to play in the basketball tournament. Each team has at least 5 players on it. If each child plays on only one team, what is the greatest number of teams that can play in the tournament?

_____

3. Complete.

a. 6 qt = _____ pt

b. 5 gal 3 qt = _____ qt

c. 35 c = _____ pt _____ c

d. 68 qt = _____ gal _____ qt

4. Measure each line segment to the neartest tenth of a centimeter.

a. _____

_____ cm

b. _____

_____ cm

c. _____

_____ cm

Multiplying by Powers of 10

Math Message

Some Powers of 10

10 * 10 * 10 * 10	10 * 10 * 10	10 * 10	10	1	.	$\frac{1}{10}$	$\frac{1}{10} * \frac{1}{10}$	$\frac{1}{10} * \frac{1}{10} * \frac{1}{10}$	$\frac{1}{10} * \frac{1}{10} * \frac{1}{10} * \frac{1}{10}$
10,000	1,000	100	10	1	.	0.1	0.01	0.001	0.0001

Multiplying by a **power of 10** is easy:

$5 * 10 = 50$ $5 * 100 = 500$ $5 * 1$ million $= 5$ million

Multiply. You may use your calculator. Look for a pattern, and develop a strategy
or rule that you can use for multiplying by powers of 10 that are greater than 1.

1. $8 * 10 = $ _____

2. $8 * 100 = $ _____

3. $8 * 1,000 = $ _____

4. $0.2 * 10 = $ _____

5. $0.2 * 100 = $ _____

6. $0.2 * 1,000 = $ _____

7. $100 * 11 = $ _____

8. $1,000,000 * 11 = $ _____

9. $0.07 * 10 = $ _____

10. $0.07 * 100,000 = $ _____

11. Describe a strategy or rule for multiplying decimals by a power of 10.

_____

_____

Multiply mentally, using your strategy. When you finish, check your answers with
your calculator.

12. $0.6 * 100 = $ _____

13. $0.03 * 10 = $ _____

14. $0.12 * 1,000 = $ _____

15. $0.005 * 100 = $ _____

16. $1.5 * 100 = $ _____

17. $0.0008 * $ _____ $= 8$

Multiplying by Powers of 10 (cont.)

Extend your powers-of-10 strategy to multiplying by 0.1, 0.01, 0.001, and so on.
These are powers of 10 that are less than 1.

Multiply using a calculator or another method (such as the estimation strategy from
the preceding lesson). Look for a pattern, and develop a strategy you can use.

18. $50 * 0.1 =$ _____

19. $5 * 0.1 =$ _____

20. $0.4 * 0.1 =$ _____

21. $0.4 * 0.01 =$ _____

22. $0.4 * 0.001 =$ _____

23. $3.2 * 0.001 =$ _____

24. $3.2 * 0.1 =$ _____

25. $3.2 * 0.01 =$ _____

26. Explain your strategy for multiplying by powers of 10 less than 1.

_____

_____

_____

_____

Recall that percents are parts of 100. You can think of the percent symbol, %, as
meaning *times* $\frac{1}{100}$ or *times 0.01*.

Example $25\% = 25 * 0.01 = 0.25$

Use your powers-of-10 strategy to rewrite each percent as an equivalent decimal.

27. $5\% =$ _____

28. $50\% =$ _____

29. $500\% =$ _____

30. $3\% =$ _____

31. $0.3\% =$ _____

32. $0.03\% =$ _____

33. $125\% =$ _____

34. $12.5\% =$ _____

35. $1\frac{1}{4}\% =$ _____

Math Boxes 2.4

1. On average, a person needs to consume $2\frac{1}{2}$ quarts of water a day.

   a. About how many pints is that? _____

   b. About how many cups? _____

   c. At this rate, about how many quarts of water would a person consume in 1 year? Circle the best estimate.

   100   1,000   10,000   100,000

2. Write each number in standard notation.

   a. $6^2 =$ _____

   b. $4^4 =$ _____

   c. $10^5 =$ _____

   d. $3^3 =$ _____

   e. $1^8 =$ _____

3. Write five names for 7.2. *Rule:* You must use addition or multiplication in each expression.

7.2

4. Divide.

   $\dfrac{378}{16} \rightarrow$ _____

5. Add or subtract.

   a.   19.03
      $+$ 17.46

   b.   941.5
      $-$ 72.9

   c.   0.5
      $+$ 0.05

   d. $12 - 4.65 =$ _____

Number-and-Word Notation for Large Numbers

When large numbers are used in newspapers, magazines, and books, they are commonly expressed with number-and-word notation, a combination of numbers and words. For example, you might read:

- There are about 3 *billion* different ways to make the first four moves in a chess game.

- There are about 25 *trillion* red blood cells in the human body.

- There are approximately 3.6 *million* 12-year-olds in the United States.

- It would cost approximately 1.4 *million* dollars to buy enough transparent tape to circle Earth at the equator.

In order to interpret and use number-and-word notation for large numbers, you need to know:

- the relationships between 1 thousand, 1 million, 1 billion, and 1 trillion (1 million = 1,000 thousand; 1 billion = 1,000 million; 1 trillion = 1,000 billion)

- how to interpret and place the decimal point

Example 1.4 million dollars may be read as "one point four million dollars." You know how much 1 million is, but how much is 0.4 million?

Since one million equals 1,000 thousand, 0.4 million is $\frac{4}{10}$ of 1,000 thousand or 400 thousand. Therefore, 1.4 million is equivalent to one million, four hundred thousand, which is written as 1,400,000 in standard notation.

"*A billion is a thousand million? Why wasn't I informed of this?*"

Fill in the blanks below.

1. a. 3 million = ____*3,000*____ thousand

  b. 5 million = _____ thousand

  c. 120 billion = _____ million

  d. 25 trillion = _____ billion

2. a. 0.3 million = ____*300*____ thousand or ____*300,000*____

  b. 27.8 million = _____ million, _____ thousand or _____

  c. 0.5 billion = _____ million or _____

  d. 10.2 billion = _____ billion, _____ million or _____

Number-and-Word Notation for Large Numbers (cont.)

Convert the numbers given in number-and-word notation to standard notation.

Example O'Hare Airport in Chicago is the busiest airport in the world. In 1998, there were approximately 72.5 million passenger departures and arrivals at O'Hare.

72,500,000 *passenger departures and arrivals*

3. The average daily circulation of *The Wall Street Journal* is approximately 1.8 million papers.

_____ papers

4. The Library of Congress in Washington, D.C., the largest library in the world, contains more than 80.0 million items.

_____ items

5. *The Codex Hammer,* one of Leonardo da Vinci's notebooks, was purchased by Bill Gates for 30.8 million dollars.

_____ dollars

Convert the numbers given in standard notation to number-and-word notation.

Example SeaWorld Adventure Park®, in Orlando, Florida, is the second most visited aquarium in the United States. Each year, approximately 5,100,000 people visit this attraction.

5.1 million people

6. Disneyland Paris®, the fourth most popular amusement park in the world, has about 11,700,000 visitors annually.

_____ visitors

7. Approximately 8,700,000,000 one-dollar bills are in circulation in the United States.

_____ one-dollar bills

8. Approximately 13,100,000,000 pennies are in circulation.

_____ pennies

9. Ross 248 is the ninth-closest star to Earth. It is approximately 61,100,000,000,000 miles away.

_____ miles

10. China, the country with the world's largest chicken population, has about 3,010,000,000 chickens.

_____ chickens

Sources: The Top Ten of Everything; The World Almanac

Date   Time

Using Benchmarks

Counts and measures in the millions, billions, and trillions are frequently in the news. Numbers this large can be confusing. They are beyond our daily experience. It can be hard to tell if they represent large or small amounts or if they are reasonable figures. It all depends on the context. For example, a million dollars is a great deal of money for one person to spend, but it is not much for a city to spend.

One way to judge the size of a large number and decide if it makes sense is to compare it to a benchmark. A **benchmark** is an important or memorable measurement, count, or number that can be used to evaluate other measurements, counts, or numbers.

Here are some benchmarks for the population of the United States:

Total population	about 275 million
Number of households	about 110 million
Number of students, Grades K–8	about 40 million
Number of students, Grade 6	about 4 million

Use the above benchmarks to decide whether the following statements are reasonable. Circle *Yes* for reasonable or *No* for not reasonable.

1. There are more than 1.75 million girls in the sixth grade in the United States.   Yes   No

2. The number of K–8 teachers in the United States is expected to climb past 20 million by the year 2000.   Yes   No

3. Every year, sixth graders spend more than 17 million dollars on school supplies.   Yes   No

4. There are 1 billion television sets in the United States.   Yes   No

5. Elementary and middle school students make up about 15% of the total population of the United States.   Yes   No

Challenge

6. To provide every student in Grades K–8 with a computer, it would cost between 35 and 75 billion dollars.   Yes   No

Use with Lesson 2.5.   **59**

Math Boxes 2.5

---

1. Complete the "What's My Rule?" table.
Rule: Multiply by 0.1.

in	out
9	
40	
0.6	
3.8	
24.7	

SRB
235

2. Use estimation to insert the decimal point in the product.

a. 5.7 * 4.4 = 2 5 0 8

b. 334 * 0.2 = 6 6 8

c. 12 * 3.65 = 4 3 8

SRB
45 46

---

3. Write each of the following numbers using digits.

a. five and fifty-five hundredths

_____

b. one hundred eight thousandths

_____

c. two hundred six and nine hundredths

_____

SRB
28

4. Divide. Show your work.

$\frac{1,556}{8} \rightarrow$ _____

SRB
22–24

---

5. The U.S. Postal Service claims that from December 1 to December 24, Americans mail an average of 78 million holiday cards per day. About how many holiday cards does the average American send during this period?

_____

Does this statistic seem reasonable?

_____

SRB
243

6. Find the mean, median, mode, and range for the following set of numbers:
12, 4, 7, 10, 0, 12, 3, 5, 1.

mean _____

median _____

mode _____

range _____

SRB
130 131

Use with Lesson 2.5.

Dividing by 2, 4, and 8

Once you know how to take one-half of a number, you can use that skill to do some division problems mentally.

- To divide a number by 2 mentally, find $\frac{1}{2}$ of the number.

    Examples   350 / 2 $\frac{1}{2}$ of 350 = 175

                    4,200 / 2 $\frac{1}{2}$ of 4,200 = 2,100

- To divide a number by 4 mentally, find $\frac{1}{2}$ of the number, and then find $\frac{1}{2}$ again.

    Examples   460 / 4 $\frac{1}{2}$ of 460 = 230; $\frac{1}{2}$ of 230 = 115

                    6,200 / 4 $\frac{1}{2}$ of 6,200 = 3,100; $\frac{1}{2}$ of 3,100 = 1,550

- To divide a number by 8 mentally, find $\frac{1}{2}$, and then $\frac{1}{2}$, and then $\frac{1}{2}$ again.

    Examples $\frac{840}{8}$ $\frac{1}{2}$ of 840 = 420; $\frac{1}{2}$ of 420 = 210; $\frac{1}{2}$ of 210 = 105

                    $\frac{496}{8}$ $\frac{1}{2}$ of 496 = 248; $\frac{1}{2}$ of 248 = 124; $\frac{1}{2}$ of 124 = 62

Use these strategies to find the following answers mentally.

1. 446 / 2 = _____

2. 640 / 4 = _____

3. 2,200 / 4 = _____

4. 440 / 8 = _____

5. 1,500 / 4 = _____

Challenge

6. $\frac{0.1}{2}$ = _____   **7.** $\frac{0.01}{2}$ = _____   **8.** $\frac{0.001}{2}$ = _____

Reading and Writing Numbers between 0 and 1

Numbers between 0 and 1 are commonly used to name very small measures. Olympic events are timed to hundredths of a second. The amounts of vitamins and minerals a person should consume each day are often measured in thousandths of a gram. The cells in our bodies are measured in millionths of a meter. In order to understand much of the world we live in, it is necessary to understand the **magnitude,** or size, of small numbers—and to be able to read and write them.

1. Complete the following table.

Decimal	Name in Words	Power of 10
0.1	one tenth	$\frac{1}{10}$
0.01		
0.001		
0.0001		
0.00001	one hundred–thousandth	$\frac{1}{10} * \frac{1}{10} * \frac{1}{10} * \frac{1}{10} * \frac{1}{10}$
0.000001		

Write the following numbers in words.

2. 0.4   _____ four tenths _____

3. 0.23   _____

4. 0.075   _____

5. 0.0109   _____

6. 0.08   _____

7. 1.54   _____

8. 24.056   _____

Challenge

9. Write the name in words for the following decimals.

   a. 0.000000001 _____   b. 0.000000000001 _____

Use with Lesson 2.6.

Reading and Writing Small Numbers

Complete the following sentences.

Example A grain of salt is about 0.004 or four <u>*thousandths*</u> of an inch long.

1. A penny weighs about 0.1 or one

   _____ of an ounce.

2. A dollar bill weighs about 0.035

   or thirty-five _____ of an ounce.

3. On average, fingernails grow at a rate of about 0.0028 or

   _____ ten-thousandths of a centimeter per day.

4. Toenails, on average, grow at a rate of about 0.0007 or

   seven _____ of a centimeter per day.

5. It takes about 0.005 or _____ of a second

   for a smell to transfer from the nose to the brain.

6. A baseball thrown by a major-league pitcher takes about 0.01 or

   one _____ of a second to cross home plate.

7. A flea weighs about 0.00017 or _____
   hundred-thousandths of an ounce.

8. A snowflake weighs about 0.00000004 or four

   _____ of an ounce.

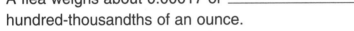

Challenge

9. About how many times heavier is a penny than a dollar bill?

   _____

10. About how many times faster do fingernails grow than toenails?

    _____

Source: The Sizesaurus

Blast from the Past

Fourth Grade

1. On average, about 10,000 babies are born in the United States each day.

   a. About how many babies are born in a week?   About _____

   b. About how many babies are born in a month?   About _____

   c. Are there more or fewer than a million
   babies born in the United States in a year?   _____

Fifth Grade

2. Complete the table.

Exponential Notation	Base	Exponent	Repeated Factors	Product
5^4	5	4	5 * 5 * 5 * 5	625
	2	3		
			6 * 6 * 6	
	2			32

Scientific notation is a useful way of writing a large or small number as the product of a number and a power of 10. Many calculators display numbers one billion or larger using scientific notation. For example, in scientific notation, 4,000 is written as $4 * 10^3$. 4,000 is equal to $4 * 1,000$. You know that 1,000 is equal to $10 * 10 * 10$, or 10^3. So 4,000 can be written as $4 * 10^3$, which is read "four times ten to the third power."

Complete the following patterns.

3. $100 = \underline{10^2}$ $200 = \underline{2 * 10^2}$

4. $1,000 = \underline{10^3}$ $3,000 = \underline{3 * 10^3}$

5. $10,000 = \underline{\hspace{3cm}}$ $40,000 = \underline{\hspace{3cm}}$

6. $100,000 = \underline{\hspace{3cm}}$ $600,000 = \underline{\hspace{3cm}}$

7. $1,000,000 = \underline{\hspace{3cm}}$ $8,000,000 = \underline{\hspace{3cm}}$

8.   10 million $= \underline{\hspace{3cm}}$ 90 million $= \underline{\hspace{3cm}}$

Use with Lesson 2.6.

Math Boxes 2.6

---

1. Solve.

a. Marta's mother is 5 times as old as Marta. Marta's mother is 25. How old is Marta? _____

b. In a few years, Marta's mother will be 3 times as old as Marta. How old will Marta be then?

_____

How old will Marta's mother be?

_____

2. Using digits, write the number three hundred forty-five million, two hundred six thousand, seventy one.

_____

SRB
4

---

3. Write each number in standard notation.

a. 1.8 million = _____

b. 0.6 billion = _____

c. 7.8 billion = _____

d. 3.7 trillion = _____

e. 0.6 trillion = _____

SRB
4

4. Multiply mentally.

a. $0.4 * 100 =$ _____

b. $0.06 * 10 =$ _____

c. _____ $= 0.13 * 1,000$

d. _____ $= 0.007 * 100$

e. $1.9 * 100 =$ _____

SRB
43 44

---

5. Multiply.

a.   3.2
   * 1.4
   ―――

b.   0.15
   *   8
   ―――

c.   5.05
   * 0.4
   ―――

SRB
45 46

Exponential Notation and the Powers Key ⌃

1. Complete the following table.

Words	Exponential Notation	Base	Exponent	Repeated Factors	Standard Notation
three to the fifth power	3^5	3	5	3 * 3 * 3 * 3 * 3	243
	7^4			7 * 7 * 7 * 7	
twenty to the third power					
				5 * 5 * 5 * 5 * 5 * 5	
ten to the *negative* fourth power	10^{-4}				

2. Complete the following table. The key sequence shown is for the TI-15.

Words	Exponential Notation	Base	Exponent	Calculator Key Sequence	Standard Notation
eight to the seventh power	8^7	8	7		2,097,152
ten to the sixth power					
	9^4				
two to the twenty-fifth power					
	10^{-3}			10 ⌃ ⊝ 3 Enter	
five to the *negative* second power					

Math Boxes 2.7

---

1. Complete the "What's My Rule?" table.
Rule: Multiply by 0.01.

in	out
7	
80	
0.4	
9.2	
32.6	

2. Use estimation to insert the decimal point in the product.

a. $0.42 * 7 =$ 2 9 4

b. $5.84 * 0.581 =$ 3 3 9 3 0 4

c. $630 * 0.063 =$ 3 9 6 9

---

3. Write each of the following numbers using digits.

a. five and seven thousandths

_____

b. two hundred and forty-nine hundredths

_____

c. fifteen and eighteen ten-thousandths

_____

4. Divide. Show your work.

$\frac{3,045}{3} \rightarrow$ _____

---

5. People in the U.S. generate about 1,100,000,000 pounds of garbage per day. About how many pounds of garbage does an average American generate each day?

_____

Does this statistic seem reasonable?

_____

6. Find the mean, median, mode, and range for the following set of numbers:
8, 2, 5, 4, 3, 10, 3.

mean _____

median _____

mode _____

range _____

Use with Lesson 2.7.

Positive and Negative Powers of 10

A **positive power of 10** is a number that can be represented as a product whose
only factors are 10s. A **negative power of 10** is a number that can be represented as
a product whose only factors are $\frac{1}{10}$ s (or 0.1s).

Examples $10^2 = 10 * 10$ The exponent tells how many times

$10^{-2} = \frac{1}{10} * \frac{1}{10} = (\frac{1}{10})^2$ 10 or $\frac{1}{10}$ is used as a factor.

1. Complete the following table.

Magnitude Benchmarks for Positive and Negative Powers of 10

Words	Standard Notation	Exponential Notation	Words	Standard Notation	Exponential Notation
one thousand	1,000	10^3	one thousandth	0.001	10^{-3}
one million		10^6	one millionth	0.000001	
one billion			one billionth		
one trillion			one trillionth		

These magnitude benchmarks can help you write other powers of 10 in exponential
and standard notation.

- To write 10^7 in standard notation, find a nearby benchmark. 10^6 is one million.
  So 10^7 will be 10 times more (10 is used as a factor one more time).

- Is 10^{-11} in the billionths or trillionths? 10^{-9} is one billionth. 10^{-12} is one trillionth.
  So 10^{-11} is in the billionths (one hundred-billionth).

2. Use benchmarks to help you complete the following table.

More Positive and Negative Powers of 10

Exponential Notation	Standard Notation	Number-and-Word Notation	Exponential Notation	Standard Notation	Number-and-Word Notation
10^4	10,000	10 thousand	10^{-4}	0.0001	1 ten-thousandth
10^8					1 hundred-thousandth
	10,000,000,000			0.0000001	

           Use with Lesson 2.8.

Translating Standard and Scientific Notation

Scientific notation is used in the following facts. Rewrite each number in standard notation. Study the example.

Example The number of taste buds in an average human mouth is about $9 * 10^3$ or ___**9,000**___ taste buds.

1. The number of hairs on an average human body is about $5 * 10^6$ or _____ hairs.

2. The width of a hair is between $2 * 10^{-7}$ and $3 * 10^{-7}$ inches or

    _____ and _____ inches.

3. The length of a grain of salt is about $1 * 10^{-5}$ or _____ meter.

4. The time it takes for a flea to take off on a vertical jump is $7.9 * 10^{-5}$ or _____ second.

Standard notation is used in the following facts. Rewrite each number in scientific notation. Study the example.

Example The approximate cost of fuel for a space shuttle mission is $2,000,000 or ___$2 * 10^6$___ dollars.

5. A Stradivarius violin, in perfect condition, sells for approximately $3,000,000 or _____ dollars.

6. The average growth rate of a child between birth and the age of 18 years is 0.007 or _____ inch per day.

7. The weight of a bee's brain is approximately 0.00004 or _____ ounce.

Challenge

8. A CD (compact disc) holds about $6 * 10^9$ bits of information. This equals about $4 * 10^5$ pages of text. By one estimate, a person's memory can hold $1 * 10^{11}$ bits of information.

    a. About how many CDs' worth of information can one person's memory hold? _____
        (unit)

    b. About how many pages of text can one person's memory hold? _____
        (unit)

Sources: The Sizesaurus; The Compass in Your Nose and Other Astonishing Facts about Humans; and Everything Has Its Price

Adding, Subtracting, and Multiplying Decimals

Use the algorithm of your choice to add, subtract, or multiply. Show your work.

1. 43.07 + 92.64 = _____

2. _____ = 29.38 + 144.2

3. 224.38 − 55.06 = _____

4. _____ = 80.402 − 3.9

5. 150 − 7.63 = _____

6. 9.06 * 4.3 = _____

7. 5.4 * 8.7 = _____

8. _____ = 0.06 * 7.9

Math Boxes 2.8

1. Solve.

   a. Sara is $\frac{1}{4}$ the age of her father. Sara's father is 60. How many years older than Sara is Sara's father?

   _____

   b. How many years ago was Sara $\frac{1}{10}$ of her father's age?

   _____

   How old was she then?

   _____

2. Using digits, write the number four billion, five hundred three million, fifty-six thousand, eight.

   _____

3. Write each number in standard notation.

   a. 12.4 million = _____

   b. 349.3 trillion = _____

   c. 0.5 trillion = _____

   d. 34.9 million = _____

   e. 569.1 million = _____

4. Multiply mentally.

   a. $0.8 * 100 =$ _____

   b. $0.03 * 10 =$ _____

   c. _____ $= 0.17 * 1,000$

   d. _____ $= 0.004 * 100$

   e. $1.6 * 100 =$ _____

5. Multiply.

   a.   5.1   **b.**   0.28   **c.**   7.55

      $* \ 2.6$ $* \ 0.03$ $* \ 0.2$

Scientific Notation on a Calculator

Use your calculator to fill in all of Column 2 first. Then fill in Columns 3 and 4 without using your calculator.

Exponential Notation	Calculator Display	Scientific Notation	Number-and-Word Notation
1. $1,000,000^2$		$1 * 10^{12}$	1 trillion
2. $10,000^3$			
3. $2,000,000^2$		$4 * 10^{12}$	
4. $20,000^3$			
5. $3,000,000^2$			
6. $30,000^3$			

Rewrite each of the following numbers in standard notation. Then enter each number into your calculator and press the $\boxed{\text{Enter}}$ key. Record the display and write each number in scientific notation.

	Standard Notation	Calculator Display	Scientific Notation
7. 456 million	_____	_____	_____
8. 3.2 trillion	_____	_____	_____
9. 23.4 billion	_____	_____	_____
10. 78 trillionths	_____	_____	_____

Solve each problem. Write each answer in standard notation and scientific notation.

11. $3,200,000 * 145,000$ _____ _____

12. 10 billion / 2.5 million _____ _____

13. $(5 * 10^4) - 10^2$ _____ _____

14. $10^2 + (3 * 10^3)$ _____ _____

15. $(8 * 10^{-1}) - 0.3$ _____ _____

16. $(4.1 * 10^8) - (3.6 * 10^6)$ _____ _____

17. $(17 * 10^{12}) / (4.25 * 10^6)$ _____ _____

18. $(6 * 10^{11}) + (7 * 10^9)$ _____ _____

Use with Lesson 2.9.

Scientific Notation on a Calculator (cont.)

Solve the number stories. Use a calculator and scientific notation to help you.

19. There are approximately 40 million students in the United States in Kindergarten through eighth grade. If, on average, each student goes to school for about 1,000 hours per year, about how many total hours do all of the students in Grades K–8 spend in school each year?

Answer _____

Number Model _____

_____

20. In 1867, the United States purchased Alaska from Russia for $7.2 million, or about 2 cents per acre. In 1994, the estimated worth of real estate in Alaska (excluding government-owned land) was $36.3 billion. About how many times more was Alaska worth in 1994 than in 1867?

Answer _____

Number Model _____

_____

21. Light travels at a speed of about 186,300 miles per second.

   a. About how many miles does light travel in one minute?

     Answer _____

     Number Model _____

   b. About how many miles does light travel in one hour?

     Answer _____

     Number Model _____

   c. About how many miles does light travel in one day?

     Answer _____

     Number Model _____

22. The average distance from the Sun to Earth is about $9.3 * 10^7$ miles and from the Sun to Mars is about $1.4 * 10^8$ miles. What is the average distance from Earth to Mars?

Answer _____

Number Model _____

Math Boxes 2.9

1. Plot each number on the number line and write the letter label for the point.

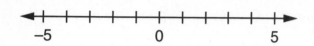

     −5   0   5

A: 1

B: −3

C: 2

D: −4

2. Write each number in standard notation.

   a. 2^{-4} = _____

   b. 5^{-3} = _____

   c. 8^{2} = _____

   d. 2^{1} = _____

   e. 10^{-5} = _____

3. Write each in standard notation.

   a. $4 * 10^{3}$ = _____

   b. _____ = $8 * 10^{5}$

   c. $12 * 10^{4}$ = _____

   d. $4.68 * 10^{3}$ = _____

   e. _____ = $3.71 * 10^{6}$

4. Divide. Show your work.

$29\overline{)697}$

5. Add or subtract. Show your work.

   a.   7.38   **b.**   9.21
        + 4.76   − 4.38

6. Build a numeral. Write
8 in the tenths place,
0 in the hundreds and ones places,
5 in the thousands place,
7 in the ten-thousands place,
9 in the hundredths place,
6 in the hundred-thousands place, and
2 in the tens place.

Answer:

_____ _____ _____ , _____ _____ _____ . _____ _____

Use with Lesson 2.9.

Practicing Division

3 Ways to Write a Division Problem

$$246 \div 12 \rightarrow 20 \text{ R6} \qquad 12\overline{)246} \rightarrow 20 \text{ R6} \qquad 246 / 12 \rightarrow 20 \text{ R6}$$

Note the arrow, →. We use it because there is a remainder.
246 / 12 = 20 R6 is not a good mathematical sentence.

Divide.

1. 74 / 6 → _____

2. 806 / 7 → _____

3. 752 / 23 → _____

4. 839 / 58 → _____

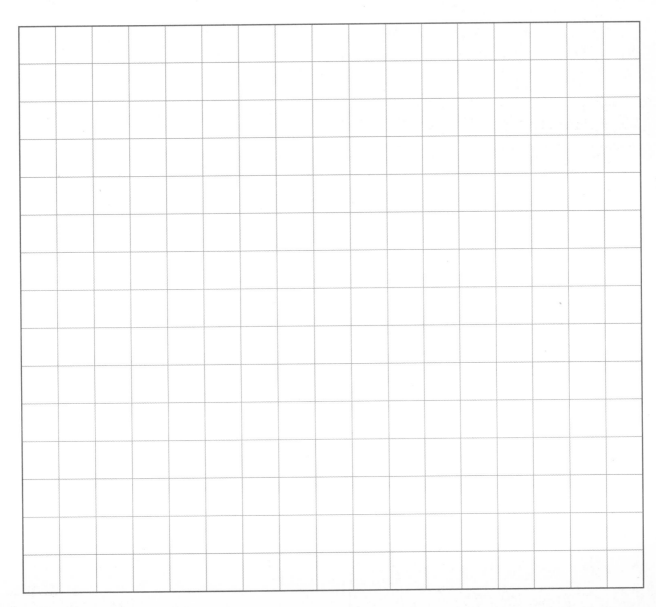

Practicing Division (cont.)

Solve the following problems mentally or with a division algorithm.

5. Four people are driving from Seattle to
San Francisco, a distance of about 810 miles.
They want to share the driving equally. About
how far should each person drive?   About _____
                                                              (unit)

6. A professional hockey stick costs about $27.
Jake's team has $546 to use for equipment.
How many hockey sticks can the team buy?
                                                    _____
                                                              (unit)

7. In 1650, it took about 50 days to sail from
London, England, to Boston, Massachusetts,
a distance of about 3,700 miles. On average,
about how many miles were sailed each day?   About _____
                                                              (unit)

8. Tutunendo, Colombia, has the greatest
annual rainfall in the world—about 464 inches
per year. On average, about how many inches
is that per month (to the nearest whole number)?   About _____
                                                              (unit)

9. It costs $42,000 to rent 1,000 square feet
of office space in a New York skyscraper
for one year. What is the cost per month?
                                                    _____
                                                              (unit)

10. A family of four spent about $3,040 on a
5-day Colorado ski vacation (transportation
not included). What was the approximate
cost of the vacation *per person per day*?   About _____
                                                              (unit)

Challenge

11. The diameter of the planet Neptune is about 30,600 miles. Pluto's diameter is
about $\frac{1}{21}$ that of Neptune. About how many miles is the diameter of Pluto?

    About _____
                    (unit)

                                                    Use with Lesson 2.10.

Math Boxes 2.10

1. Solve. Helen is 3 years older than her brother Michael.

  a. If Michael is 5, how old is Helen?

  _____

  b. If Helen is 18, how old is Michael?

  _____

  c. If Helen is twice as old as Michael, how

  old is Helen? _____

  d. If Michael is $\frac{1}{4}$ as old as Helen,
  how old is Michael?

  _____

2. Using digits, write the number twenty-six billion, two hundred eight million, seventy-one thousand, three hundred forty-two with digits.

  _____

3. Convert the following numbers in standard notation to number-and-word notation.

  a. 4,600,000 = _____

  b. 3,700,000,000 = _____

  c. 8,340,000 = _____

4. Multiply mentally.

  a. $0.9 * 100 =$ _____

  b. $0.08 * 10 =$ _____

  c. _____ $= 0.14 * 1,000$

  d. _____ $= 0.002 * 100$

  e. $1.3 * 100 =$ _____

5. Multiply.

  a. 2.6
     * 5.1
     ─────

  b. 0.56
     * 12
     ─────

  c. 5.07
     * 21
     ─────

Estimating and Calculating Quotients

For each problem:

- Estimate the quotient by using numbers that are close to the numbers given and that are easy to divide. Write your estimate. Then write a number sentence showing how you estimated.

- Ignore any decimal points. Divide as if the numbers were whole numbers.

- Use your estimate to insert a decimal point in the final answer.

1. $4\overline{)68.8}$

Estimate _____

_____
How I estimated

Answer _____

2. $8\overline{)27.2}$

Estimate _____

_____
How I estimated

Answer _____

3. $\$18.55 \div 7$

Estimate _____

_____
How I estimated

Answer _____

4. $5.61 \div 3$

Estimate _____

_____
How I estimated

Answer _____

5. $16\overline{)94.4}$

Estimate _____

_____
How I estimated

Answer _____

6. $14\overline{)116.2}$

Estimate _____

_____
How I estimated

Answer _____

Use with Lesson 2.11.

Whole-Number Division with Decimal Answers

1. Seven people had lunch. The bill was $29. Divide $29 into 7 equal shares. How much is one share, in dollars and cents?

   _____

2. Find 8 ÷ 3. Give the answer as a decimal with one digit after the decimal point.

   _____

3. Find 114 / 40. Give the answer as a decimal with two digits after the decimal point.

   _____

4. A board 125 centimeters long is cut into 12 pieces of equal length. What is the length of each piece, to the nearest tenth of a centimeter?

   _____

5. Find 26 / 19. Give the answer as a decimal with two digits after the decimal point.

   _____

6. A 2-meter ribbon is cut into 6 pieces of equal size. What is the length of each piece, to the nearest tenth of a centimeter? *Hint:* How many centimeters are in 1 meter?

   _____

Math Boxes 2.11

---

1. Plot each number on the number line and write the letter label for the point.

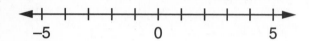

−5   0   5

A: −1

B: 3

C: −2

D: 4

2. Write each number in standard notation.

a. $4^{-3} =$ _____

b. $3^{-2} =$ _____

c. $2^8 =$ _____

d. $1^2 =$ _____

e. $10^{-3} =$ _____

---

3. Write each in scientific notation.

a. $7,000 =$ _____

b. _____ $= 900,000$

c. $250,000 =$ _____

d. $2,960 =$ _____

e. _____ $= 50,800$

4. Divide. Show your work.

$46\overline{)552}$

---

5. Add or subtract. Show your work.

a.
$$\begin{array}{r} 9.59 \\ + 3.66 \\ \hline \end{array}$$

b.
$$\begin{array}{r} 8.01 \\ - 5.82 \\ \hline \end{array}$$

6. Build a numeral. Write
6 in the hundredths place,
5 in the tens place,
4 in the ten-thousands place,
9 in the hundreds place,
1 in the ones place, and
0s where you need them.

Answer:

—— ——,—— —— ——.—— ——

Use with Lesson 2.11.

Time to Reflect

1. How good do you think you are at each of the skills listed below?
   Check the most appropriate box.

Skill	I'm very good.	I'm pretty good.	I need some practice.	I need a lot of practice.
a. Adding and subtracting decimals				
b. Multiplying decimals				
c. Dividing whole numbers				
d. Dividing with decimals				
e. Estimating products in multiplication with decimals				
f. Estimating quotients in division with decimals				

2. When you learn how to do something in mathematics, such as divide with decimals, would you rather learn just one method that works all the time or learn several methods that work all the time? Explain.

_____

_____

_____

_____

Math Boxes 2.12

1. **a.** Plot the following points on the grid.

  A: (3,4)   **B:** (1,0)   **C:** (4,−3)

  D: (−3,−2)   **E:** (−1,3)

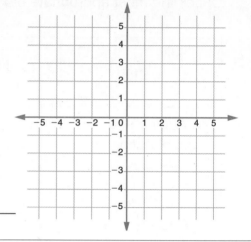

  b. Draw line segments connecting points
  A to *B*, *B* to *C*, *C* to *D*, *D* to *E*, and *E* to *A*.

  c. What kind of polygon is this? _____

  d. Is it a convex or concave polygon? _____

---

2. A faucet drips at the rate of 2 fluid
ounces per hour. At this rate:

  a. How many hours
  would it take to fill
  a 1-cup container? _____

  b. How many hours
  would it take to fill
  a 1-quart container? _____

  c. How many 1-cup
  containers would
  be filled in 1 day? _____

3. Complete the "What's My Rule?" table.
Rule: Multiply by 100.

in	out
	50
	160
0.08	
0.002	
0.007	

---

4. Reshi's brother was 8 years old
when Reshi was born. Reshi's
brother is now twice as old as
Reshi. How old is Reshi now? _____

Explain how you got your answer.

_____

_____

_____

_____

5. Plot each number on the number line and
write the letter label for the point.

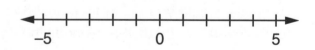

  A: 1   **B:** −1

  C: 5   **D:** −5

Math Boxes 3.1

1. Rename each fraction as a mixed or a whole number.

a. $\frac{5}{4} =$ _____

b. $\frac{5}{3} =$ _____

c. $\frac{11}{6} =$ _____

d. $\frac{5}{5} =$ _____

e. $\frac{14}{4} =$ _____

SRB
67

2. Divide. Do not use a calculator.

$6\overline{)93.6}$

SRB
50–53

3. Complete the "What's My Rule?" table.
Rule: Add 0.58

in	out
7	
1.79	
0.9	
	4.62
	3.15

SRB
235

4. Write each number in number-and-word notation.

a. 200,000

_____

b. 16,900,000,000

_____

c. 58,400,000,000,000

_____

SRB
4

5. Use your calculator to complete the table.

Problem	Scientific Notation	Standard Notation
$100,000^3$	$1 * 10^{15}$	1,000,000,000,000,000
$9,000,000^2$		
$20,000^5$		
$30^4 + 30^4$		
$30^7 + 70^3$		

SRB
7 8

Patterns and Variables

Study the number sentences at the right. All three sentences show the same **general pattern.**

$$10\% \text{ of } 50 = \frac{10}{100} * 50$$
$$10\% \text{ of } 200 = \frac{10}{100} * 200$$
$$10\% \text{ of } 8 = \frac{10}{100} * 8$$

- This general pattern may be described in words: To find 10% of a number, multiply the number by $\frac{10}{100}$ (or 0.10 or $\frac{1}{10}$).

- The pattern may also be described by a number sentence that contains a variable: 10% of $n = \frac{10}{100} * n$.

  A **variable** is a symbol—such as n, x, A, or $\square$. A variable can stand for any one of many possible numerical values in a number sentence.

- Number sentences like 10% of $50 = \frac{10}{100} * 50$ and 10% of $200 = \frac{10}{100} * 200$ are examples, or **special cases,** for the general pattern described by 10% of $n = \frac{10}{100} * n$.

To write a special case for a general pattern, you replace the variable with a number.

For example

General pattern   10% of $n = \frac{10}{100} * n$

Special case   10% of $35 = \frac{10}{100} * 35$

---

1. Here are three special cases for a general pattern.

   $$\frac{10}{10} = 1 \qquad \frac{725}{725} = 1 \qquad \frac{\frac{1}{2}}{\frac{1}{2}} = 1$$

   a. Describe the pattern in words.

   _____

   b. Give two other special cases for the pattern.

   _____   _____

2. Here are three special cases for another general pattern.

   $$15 + (-15) = 0 \qquad 3 + (-3) = 0 \qquad \tfrac{1}{4} + (-\tfrac{1}{4}) = 0$$

   a. Describe the pattern in words.

   _____

   b. Give two other special cases for the pattern.

   _____   _____

Patterns and Variables (cont.)

3. A spider has 8 legs. The general pattern is: S spiders have $S * 8$ legs.
   Write two special cases for the general pattern.

   a. _____   b. _____

4. Study the following special cases for a general pattern.

   The value of 6 quarters is $\frac{6}{4}$ dollars.

   The value of 10 quarters is $\frac{10}{4}$ dollars.

   The value of 33 quarters is $\frac{33}{4}$ dollars.

   a. Describe the general pattern in words.

   _____

   b. Give two other special cases for the pattern.

   _____

   _____

Write three special cases for each general pattern.

5. $p + p = 2 * p$

   _____

   _____

   _____

6. $C * \frac{1}{C} = 1$

   _____

   _____

   _____

7. $p + p + (3 * p) = 5 * p$

   _____

   _____

   _____

8. $s^2 + s = (s + 1) * s$

   _____

   _____

   _____

Writing General Patterns

Here is a way to find the general pattern for a group of special cases.

Example Write the general pattern for the special cases at the right.

$$8 / 1 = 8$$
$$12.5 / 1 = 12.5$$
$$0.3 / 1 = 0.3$$

Solution Strategy

Step 1 Write everything that is the same for all of the special cases.

Use blanks for the parts that change.

_____ / 1 = _____

Each special case has division by 1 and an equal sign.

Step 2 Fill in the blanks. Each special case has a different number, but the number is the same for both blanks, so use the same variable in both blanks.

Possible solutions: $N / 1 = N$ or $x / 1 = x$ or $\square / 1 = \square$

Write a general pattern for each group of three special cases.

1. $18 * 1 = 18$

$2.75 * 1 = 2.75$

$\frac{6}{10} * 1 = \frac{6}{10}$

General pattern _____

2. $6 * 0 = 0$

$\frac{1}{2} * 0 = 0$

$78.7 * 0 = 0$

General pattern _____

3. 1 cat has $1 * 4$ legs.

2 cats have $2 * 4$ legs.

5 cats have $5 * 4$ legs.

General pattern _____

4. $6 * 6 = 6^2$

$\frac{1}{2} * \frac{1}{2} = \left(\frac{1}{2}\right)^2$

$0.7 * 0.7 = (0.7)^2$

General pattern _____

Math Boxes 3.2

1. Mark and label each fraction on the number line.

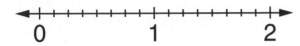

0   1   2

a. $\frac{1}{4}$

b. $1\frac{1}{8}$

c. $1\frac{3}{8}$

d. $\frac{3}{2}$

SRB 64

2. Multiply. Do not use a calculator.

$3.42 * 6 =$ _____

SRB 45 46

3. List all the factors of each number.

a. 30 _____

b. 24 _____

c. 19 _____

d. 56 _____

SRB 10

4. Write in standard notation.

a. 5^{-4} _____

b. 4^{-1} _____

c. $5 * 10^{-3}$ _____

d. $6 * 10^{-2}$ _____

SRB 8

5. Three special cases of a pattern are given below. Using one variable, write a number sentence to describe the general pattern.

a. $(6 + 5) * 3 = (15 - 4) * 3$

b. $(6 + 5) * 2 = (15 - 4) * 2$

c. $(6 + 5) * 12 = (15 - 4) * 12$

General pattern:

_____

SRB 101

6. Find the mean, median, mode, and range for the following set of numbers:

6, 9, 9, 8, 3, 1

mean _____

median _____

mode _____

range _____

SRB 130 131

General Patterns with Two Variables

Math Message

This general pattern uses two variables.
They are *a* and *b*.

To write a special case for the general pattern:

• Replace the variable *a* with any number.

• Replace the variable *b* with any number.

Notice that in the third special case,
the variables *a* and *b* have been
replaced by the same number.

General Pattern
$a * (b - 1) = a * b - a$
Special Cases
$5 * (4 - 1) = 5 * 4 - 5$
$72 * (13 - 1) = 72 * 13 - 72$
$6 * (6 - 1) = 6 * 6 - 6$

Write three special cases for each general pattern.

1. $X * Y = Y * X$

_____

_____

_____

2. $p * \frac{n}{n} = p$

_____

_____

_____

3. $x * 0 = y * 0$

_____

_____

_____

4. $\frac{a}{b} * \frac{b}{a} = 1$ (*a* and *b* are not 0.)

_____

_____

_____

5. $A + A + B = 2 * (A + B) - B$

_____

_____

_____

6. $(r + s) + (5 - s) = r + 5$

_____

_____

_____

Use with Lesson 3.2.

General Patterns with Two Variables (cont.)

Example Write a general pattern with two variables for the
         special cases at the right.

$$7 + 3 = 3 + 7$$

$$\frac{1}{2} + \frac{3}{2} = \frac{3}{2} + \frac{1}{2}$$

$$4 + (-2) = -2 + 4$$

Solution Strategy

Step 1 Write everything that is the same for
         all of the special cases. Use blanks
         for the parts that change.

_____ + _____ = _____ + _____

Each special case has two additions and an equal sign.

Step 2 Each special case has two different
         numbers. Use different variables
         (letters or other symbols) for the
         numbers that vary. Write them
         on the blanks.

$$\underline{\ a\ } + \underline{\ b\ } = \underline{\ b\ } + \underline{\ a\ }$$

Step 3 Check that the special cases
         given fit the general pattern.

Write a number sentence with two variables for each general pattern.

1. $4 * \frac{2}{7} = 2 * \frac{4}{7}$

$10 * \frac{2}{3} = 2 * \frac{10}{3}$

$29 * \frac{2}{8} = 2 * \frac{29}{8}$

General pattern _____

2. $(5 * 2) + (5 * 6) = 5 * (2 + 6)$

$(5 * 4) + (5 * 1) = 5 * (4 + 1)$

$(5 * 2) + (5 * 100) = 5 * (2 + 100)$

General pattern _____

_____

3. Write a general pattern using variables.
   Let d = number of dogs.
   Let b = number of birds.

   3 dogs and 5 birds have
   $(3 * 4) + (5 * 2)$ legs.

   5 dogs and 9 birds have
   $(5 * 4) + (9 * 2)$ legs.

   17 dogs and 6 birds have
   $(17 * 4) + (6 * 2)$ legs.

   _____

   _____

4. For the general pattern $x^2 * y^2 = (x * y)^2$,
   write the special case.

   a. $x = 4$ and $y = 5$

   _____

   b. $x = 10$ and $y = 10$

   _____

   c. Is the general pattern true,
      no matter which numbers
      you use? _____

Algebraic Expressions

A variable is a symbol—such as *y, Y, K,* or ☐. A variable can stand for any one of many possible numerical values in a given problem. A variable can also represent a specific unknown number.

Example On November 1, Denise was able to tread water for 5 minutes longer than she could on September 1. How long could Denise tread water on November 1?

Solution Strategy
Because you don't know how long Denise tread water on September 1, you can't tell how long she tread water on November 1. However, if you use the variable *t* to represent her time on September 1 in minutes, you can represent her time on November 1 as *t* + 5 minutes.

t + 5 is an **algebraic expression.** An algebraic expression contains at least one variable. It may contain numbers, operation symbols (+, −, *, or /), and grouping symbols (such as parentheses). Like a variable, an algebraic expression can stand for a range of numerical values or a specific number that is not known.

To **evaluate an algebraic expression** means to give a numerical value to each variable and then calculate the value of the expression. For example, if *t* = 4, you would evaluate *t* + 5 as 4 + 5, or 9.

Complete each of the following statements with an algebraic expression, using the suggested variable. Study the first one.

1. If a large pizza costs $4.25 more than a small pizza, then a large pizza costs

   <u>   *D* + $4.25   </u>.

A small pizza costs *D* dollars.   large pizza

2. a. If Boris's hamster is 12 months older than his goldfish, then his goldfish is

   _____ months old.

   b. Evaluate your expression: If Boris's hamster is 21 months old, how old is his goldfish?

   _____

Boris's hamster is *h* months old.   Boris's goldfish

Algebraic Expressions (cont.)

3. a. The weight of 5 bags of candy is

_____ pounds.

A bag of candy
weighs *P* pounds.

   b. If every member of your class had a bag of candy, how
       many pounds of candy would there be?

_____

_____

4. If the whale dives 85 feet, it will be at a depth of

_____ feet.

The whale is at a
depth of *M* feet.

5. a. During lunch, the cafeteria is divided into 3 parts,
        with each part having an equal floor area. Each part

has an area of _____ ft^2.

   b. If the area of the cafeteria floor is 2,400 square feet,
       what is the area of each of the 3 parts?

_____
        (unit)

The cafeteria floor
has an area of *A* ft^2.

Challenge

6. The charge for a book that
    is *d* days overdue is

_____ cents.

A library charges 5 cents for
each day a book is overdue,
plus an additional 10-cent
service charge.

7. a. If James spends $\frac{5}{6}$ of his weekly allowance seeing a movie,

he has _____ dollars of his allowance left.

   b. If a movie ticket costs $7.50,
       what is James's weekly allowance? _____

James's weekly
allowance is *x* dollars.

Division Practice

For Problems 1–4:

- Estimate the quotient. Write a number sentence to show how you estimated.

- Divide. Give the answer to two decimal places. Use your estimate to place the decimal point in your answer.

1. 8)983   Estimate _____

    _____
    How I estimated

    Answer _____

2. 12)437   Estimate _____

    _____
    How I estimated

    Answer _____

3. 46)728   Estimate _____

    _____
    How I estimated

    Answer _____

4. 11)652   Estimate _____

    _____
    How I estimated

    Answer _____

For Problems 5 and 6:

- Estimate the quotient. Write a number sentence to show how you estimated.

- Ignore the decimal point and divide. *Disregard any remainder.*

- Use your estimate to place the decimal point in your answer.

5. 5)315.8   Estimate _____

    _____
    How I estimated

    Answer _____

6. 8)204.6   Estimate _____

    _____
    How I estimated

    Answer _____

Use with Lesson 3.3.

Math Boxes 3.3

---

1. Rename each fraction as a mixed or whole number.

a. $\frac{3}{2} =$ _____

b. $\frac{7}{6} =$ _____

c. $\frac{11}{8} =$ _____

d. $\frac{6}{6} =$ _____

e. $\frac{10}{4} =$ _____

---

2. Divide.

$8\overline{)99.2}$

---

3. Complete the "What's My Rule?" table.
Rule: Subtract 1.32

in	out
8	
2.15	
1.8	
	3.57
	6.01

---

4. Write each number in number-and-word notation.

a. 4,800,000

_____

b. 56,000,000

_____

c. 3,856,000,000

_____

---

5. Use your calculator to complete the table.

Problem	Scientific Notation	Standard Notation
$300,000^2$		
$800^4 - 400^2$		
$10^7 * 10^7$		
$80^4 + 40^8$		
$\frac{70^{12}}{70^4}$		

Formulas

You are familiar with formulas in mathematics.

Formula for the perimeter of a square:	Formula for the area of a parallelogram:
$p = 4 * s$	$A = b * h$

A **formula** expresses a relationship among quantities. The quantities are represented by variables. In the first formula above, the variable p stands for the perimeter, and the variable s stands for the length of any side. In the second formula, A stands for the area, b for the length of the base, and h for the height of the parallelogram.

A formula is usually written with an equal sign (=), a variable on one side of the equal sign, and an algebraic expression on the other side. Formulas may or may not include numbers.

The variables in a formula are usually the first letters of the quantities they stand for: "A" for area, "b" for length of the base, "h" for height, and so on. You can think of a formula as a rule for finding the value of something.

Example

The perimeter p of a rectangle can be found by the formula $p = 2 * (b + h)$. Find the perimeter if $b = 4.5$ inches and $h = 8.5$ inches.

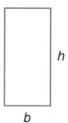

Solution Strategy

Substitute 4.5 inches for b and 8.5 inches for h in the formula:
$$p = 2 * (b + h)$$
$$= 2 * (4.5 \text{ in.} + 8.5 \text{ in.})$$
$$= 2 * (13 \text{ in.})$$
$$= 26 \text{ in.}$$

1. The formula $F = (1.8 * C) + 32$ can be used to convert degrees Celsius to degrees Fahrenheit.

   a. 10°C is _____ °F.   **b.** 0°C is _____ °F.   **c.** 30°C is _____ °F.

2. The area of the shaded region between the two squares in the diagram can be found by the formula $A = W^2 - w^2$. Find the area of the shaded region if $W = 20$ inches and $w = 9$ inches.

   Be careful! The capital W and the lowercase w stand for different lengths.

   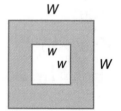

   _____ in.²

Date _____ Time _____

Evaluating Formulas

1. The formula $A = \frac{1}{2} * b * h$ can be used to find the area of a triangle. *A* stands for the area, *b* for the length of the base, and *h* for the height of the triangle.

   Find the area of a triangle with *b* = 4 cm and *h* = 2.5 cm. _____ cm²

2. The formula $C = 2 * \pi * r$ can be used to find the circumference of a circle, where *C* is the circumference and *r* is the radius.

   a. What is the circumference of
      a circle with a radius of 1 foot?   _____ ft

   b. What is the circumference of
      a circle with a radius of 12 inches? _____ in.

3. The formula $c = 1.3 * t$ can be used to find the average number of calories a typical adult uses while lying in bed resting. The variable *t* represents the number of minutes a person is resting, and *c* is the number of calories used while resting.

   a. How many calories does a resting person use in 12 minutes? _____
      (unit)

   b. How many calories does that person use in 120 seconds? _____
      (unit)

4. The size of the screen on a television set or computer monitor is reported as its diagonal length. For example, the screen on a 17-inch monitor has a diagonal length of 17 inches.

   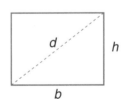

   The two formulas at the right show how $b = 0.8 * d$
   the diagonal length *d*, the base length *b*, $h = 0.6 * d$
   and the height *h* are related.

   Find the base length and the height of a 21-inch television screen.

   a. Base _____
            (unit)

   b. Height _____
            (unit)

   You have been evaluating formulas. To **evaluate** a formula means to obtain a numerical value for one of its variables by substituting numerical values for all of the other variables and then doing the calculations indicated in the formula.

"What's My Rule?"

Complete each table according to the rule. Use a calculator if you wish.

1. *Rule:* Add -4.9 to the "in" number.

in	out
-8	
17	
9.5	
	-13.9
	26

2. *Rule:* $b = 4 / a$

a	b
2	
$\frac{1}{2}$	
5	
	1
	$\frac{1}{2}$

3. *Rule:* Subtract 6.3 from the "in" number.

in	out
-15	
37	
	4
-20	-26.3
0.3	

4. *Rule:* $n = 0.5 * m$

m	n
2	
10	
0.8	
	0.5
	3

5. a. State in words the rule for the "What's My Rule?" table at the right.

_____

_____

b. Circle the formula that describes the rule.

$t - 15 = s$ $t + s = 15$ $15 + t = s$

s	t
9.5	5.5
$\frac{15}{2}$	$\frac{15}{2}$
7	8
$\frac{3}{4}$	$14\frac{1}{4}$
-10	25

Math Boxes 3.4

---

1. Mark and label each fraction on the number line.

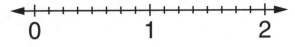

a. $\frac{5}{10}$

b. $\frac{7}{4}$

c. $\frac{7}{8}$

d. $\frac{15}{16}$

2. Multiply. Do not use a calculator.

$9 * 4.27 = $ _____

---

3. List all the factors of each number.

a. 12 _____

b. 25 _____

c. 36 _____

d. 29 _____

4. Write in standard notation.

a. 2^{-3} _____

b. 8^{-2} _____

c. $2 * 10^{-3}$ _____

d. $8 * 10^{-1}$ _____

---

5. Three special cases of a pattern are given below. Using one variable, write a number sentence to describe the general pattern.

a. $4 + 4 - 9 = (2 * 4) - 3^2$

b. $8 + 8 - 9 = (2 * 8) - 3^2$

c. $3.5 + 3.5 - 9 = (2 * 3.5) - 3^2$

General pattern:

_____

6. Find the mean, median, and range for the following set of numbers:

13, 16, 12, 11, 18, 20

mean _____

median _____

range _____

Representing Speed

Math Message

Ever since the early years of the automobile, police have been trying to catch speeding motorists. At first, officers were equipped with bicycles and stopwatches. They hid behind trees or rocks and emerged to pursue offenders. An Englishman, Lord Montague of Beaulieu, received a ticket for driving 12 miles per hour.

"Eagle Eye" Gus Schalkman, the pride of the Bronx, holds the record for ticket writing. He got his 135th car today on his post near the Queensboro bridge, Aug. 14,1929.

1. At a speed of 12 miles per hour, about how many miles could Lord Montague travel in 1 minute? _____ mi

2. Tell how you solved this problem. _____

    _____

    Source: Beyond Belief!

3. Complete the table. Use the formula $d = 0.2 * t$.

    A car traveling at a speed of 12 miles per hour is traveling 0.2 mile per minute. You can use the following rule to calculate the distance traveled for any number of minutes.

    | Distance traveled (d) | = | 0.2 mile per minute | * | number of minutes (t) |

    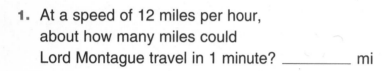

    or the formula
    $d = 0.2 * t$

    where d stands for the distance traveled in miles and t for the time of travel in minutes.

    For example, in 1 minute, the car will travel 0.2 mile (0.2 * 1). In 2 minutes, it will travel 0.4 mile (0.2 * 2).

Time (min) t	Distance (mi) $0.2 * t$
1	0.2
2	0.4
3	
4	
5	
6	
7	
8	
9	
10	

Use with Lesson 3.5.

Representing Speed (cont.)

4. Complete the graph using the table on page 98. Connect the points.

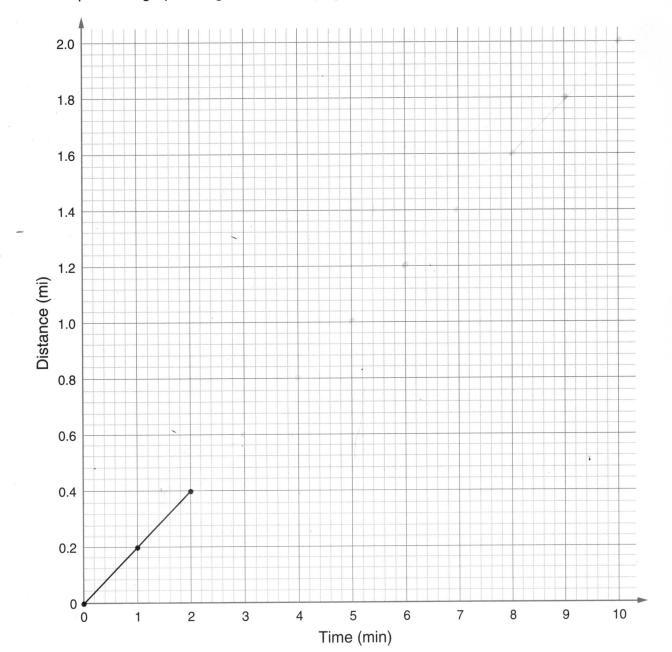

Time (min)

Use your graph to answer the following questions.

5. a. About how far would the car travel in $1\frac{1}{2}$ minutes?   About _____
   (unit)

   b. About how many miles would the car
      travel in 5 minutes 24 seconds (about $5\frac{1}{2}$ minutes)?   About _____
   (unit)

6. About how long would it take the car to travel 5 miles?   About _____
   (unit)

Representing Rates

Complete each table. Then graph the data. Connect the points.

1. Emma earns $6 per hour.

   Rule:
   Earnings = $6 per hour * number of hours worked

   Formula:
   $E = 6 * h$

Time (hr) h	Earnings ($) 6 * h
1	
2	
3	
	27
7	

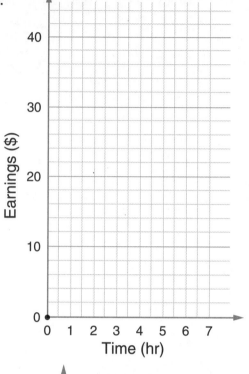

a. Plot a point to show Emma's earnings for $5\frac{1}{2}$ hours.

b. How much would she earn? _____

2. A young blue whale can gain as much as 300 pounds per day.

   Rule:
   Weight gained = 300 pounds per day * number of days

   Formula:
   $W = 300 * t$

Time (days) t	Weight gained (lb) 300 * t
1	
2	
3	
	1,425
6	

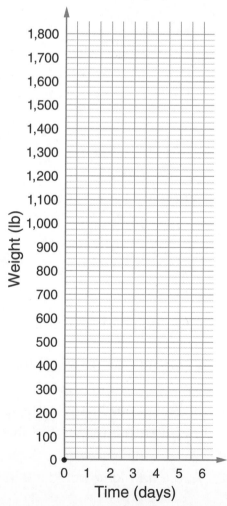

a. Plot a point to show the number of pounds a young blue whale can gain in 36 hours.

b. How many pounds is that? _____

Source: Beyond Belief!

Use with Lesson 3.5.

Representing Rates (cont.)

3. Chewy candies cost $1.50 a pound.

Rule:
Cost = $1.50 per pound * number of pounds

Formula:
c = 1.50 * w

Weight (lb) w	Cost ($) 1.50 * w
1	
2	
3	
	15.00
12	

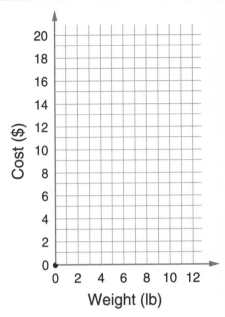

a. Plot a point to show the cost of 8 pounds.

b. How much would 8 pounds cost? _____

4. The average 11-year-old reads about 11 pages of text per day.

Rule:
Pages read = 11 pages per day * number of days

Formula:
p = 11 * t

Time (days) t	Pages 11 * t
1	
2	
3	
	44
5$\frac{1}{2}$	

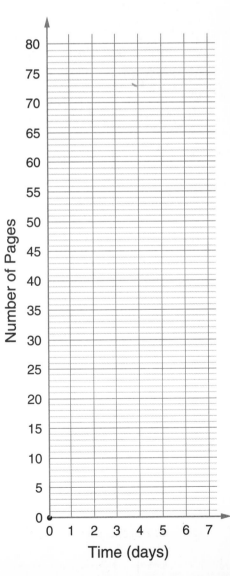

a. Plot a point to show how many pages of text an average 11-year-old reads in a week.

b. How many pages is that? _____

Source: Astounding Averages

Math Boxes 3.5

1. Rename each fraction as an equivalent fraction.

    a. $\frac{1}{4}$ = _____

    b. $\frac{1}{2}$ = _____

    c. $\frac{1}{10}$ = _____

    d. $\frac{6}{8}$ = _____

    e. $\frac{4}{5}$ = _____

SRB
68

2. Divide. Do not use a calculator.

    $12\overline{)57.6}$

SRB
50–53

3. The time of day varies from time zone to time zone. The time difference between Newark, New Jersey, and Seattle, Washington, is given by the formula $N - S = 3$, where N stands for the time in Newark and S for the time in Seattle.

    a. If $S = 8$ P.M., $N =$ _____.

    b. If $N = 8$ P.M., $S =$ _____.

    c. If $S = 11$ A.M., $N =$ _____.

SRB
227 228

4. Write in standard notation.

    a. $5^6 =$ _____

    b. $4^5 =$ _____

    c. $5 * 10^3 =$ _____

    d. $6 * 10^4 =$ _____

SRB
8

5. Give three special cases for the general pattern $\frac{0}{k} = k - k$.

_____

_____

_____

SRB
101

6. Michael is 5 years younger than Misha and 3 years older than Gary.

    a. Who is the oldest? _____

    b. If Gary is 12 years old, how old is Michael? _____

    How old is the oldest of the three?

    _____

SRB
222

Use with Lesson 3.5.

Falling Objects

The picture at the right was redrawn from flash photographs of a falling golf ball. The time interval between flashes was $\frac{1}{20}$ second.

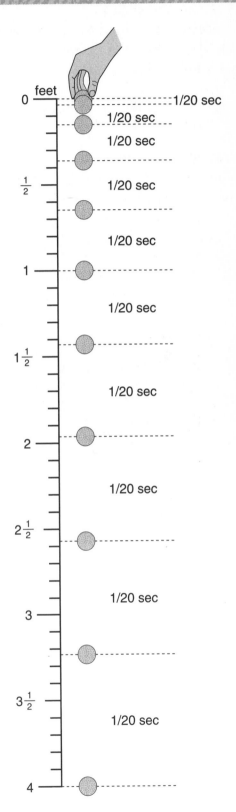

Elapsed Time (sec)	Total Distance Fallen (ft)
$\frac{1}{20}$	0.04
$\frac{2}{20}$	0.16
$\frac{3}{20}$	0.36
$\frac{4}{20}$	0.64
$\frac{5}{20}$	1.00
$\frac{6}{20}$	1.44
$\frac{7}{20}$	1.96
$\frac{8}{20}$	2.56
$\frac{9}{20}$	3.24
$\frac{10}{20}$	4.00

1. How far did the ball fall during the first $\frac{1}{4}$ second? _____

2. How far had it fallen after $\frac{1}{2}$ second? _____

3. Check the statement that you believe is true.

   _____ A ball falls at a constant (even) speed.

   _____ As a ball falls, it picks up speed.

What Happens When an Object Is Dropped?

Galileo was an Italian physicist who lived from 1564 to 1642. His work led to the following rule for the distance traveled by a freely falling object:

Distance traveled in feet $=$ 16 $*$ square of the elapsed time in seconds

Written as a formula, the rule is $d = 16 * t * t$; or $d = 16 * t^2$, where d is the distance traveled by the object in feet and t is the time in seconds that has elapsed since the object started falling. For example, after 1 second, an object will have traveled 16 feet (16 * 1 * 1); after 2 seconds, it will have traveled 64 feet (16 * 2 * 2).

Galileo's formula really applies only in a vacuum, where there is no air resistance to slow an object's fall. However, it is a good approximation for the fall of a dense object, such as a bowling ball, over a fairly short distance.

1. The following table shows the approximate distance traveled by a freely falling object at 1-second intervals. Use Galileo's formula to complete the table.

Elapsed time (sec) t	0	1	2	3	4	5	6	7	8	9
Distance (ft) $16 * t^2$	0	16	64	144						

2. Graph the data from the table above onto the grid on page 105.

3. Use the graph to estimate the number of seconds it takes an object to fall 500 feet, ignoring air resistance.　　About _____ seconds

Challenge

4. a. About how many seconds would it take an object to fall 1 mile, ignoring air resistance? Use your calculator. (*Hint:* 1 mile = 5,280 feet)　　About _____ seconds

   b. In the table at the right, evaluate Galileo's distance formula for at least two other values of t (time).

t		
$16 * t^2$		

Use with Lesson 3.6.

What Happens When an Object Is Dropped? (cont.)

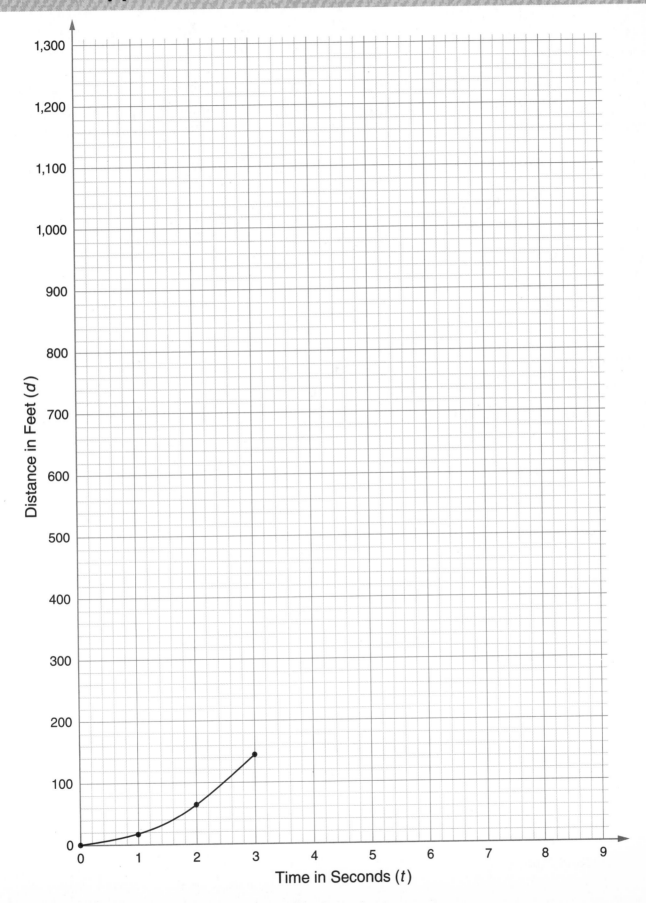

Distance in Feet (d)

Time in Seconds (t)

Use with Lesson 3.6.

What Happens When an Object Is Dropped? (cont.)

The speed of a freely falling object increases the longer it continues to fall. The speed of a falling object at any given instant can be calculated by using the rule

speed in feet per second = 32 * elapsed time in seconds,

or by using the formula, $s = 32 * t$

where s is the speed of the object in feet per second and t is the elapsed time in seconds since the object started falling.

For example, after 1 second, the object is traveling at a speed of about 32 feet per second (32 * 1); and after 2 seconds, at a speed of about 64 feet per second (32 * 2).

5. Use this formula to complete the table. Then graph the data in the table.

Elapsed time (sec) t	Speed (ft per sec) $32 * t$
1	32
2	64
3	
4	
5	
6	

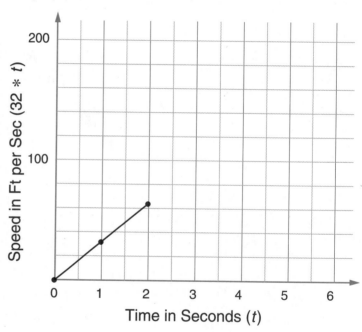

6. At about what speed would an object be traveling 18 seconds after it started falling?

About _____ ft per sec

7. If a freely falling object is traveling at a speed of 290 feet per second, about how long has it been falling?

About _____ sec

Use with Lesson 3.6.

Math Boxes 3.6

1. a. Name the least common
multiple of 4, 6, and 8. _____

b. Name the least common
multiple of 3, 12, and 15. _____

c. Name the least common
multiple of 6, 8, and 9. _____

2. Multiply. Do not use a calculator.

$5.3 * 9.1 =$ _____

3. Complete the table. Then graph the data and connect
the points.

Samantha earns \$9 for each yard she mows.
Rule: Earnings = \$9 * number of yards mowed

Number of yards (y)	Earnings (\$) (9 * y)
1	
2	
3	
	45
6	

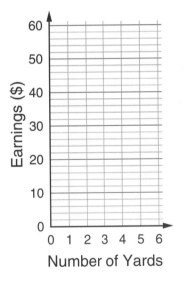

Number of Yards

4. The area *A* of a circle can be
found by the formula $A = \pi * r^2$.

a. Find the area if
$r = 3.7$ centimeters.

_____ cm²

b. Find the area if $r = 9$ inches.

_____ in.²

5. Give three special cases for the general
pattern below.

$(b * h) + 4 = 4 + (h * b)$

_____

_____

_____

Variables and Formulas in Spreadsheets

A typical computer spreadsheet has **columns,** identified by letters, and **rows,** identified by numbers. Columns and rows intersect to form boxes called **cells.**

Each cell in a spreadsheet is named by the letter of the column and the number of the row it is in. For example, Cell A1 is in Column A, Row 1. There is no space in the name between the letter and the number. Cells can contain text, numbers, or nothing at all.

Example The spreadsheet at the right shows the number of hits made and runs scored by players on a softball team. The statistics are for the first five games played. As more games are played, the numbers will be updated.

	A	B	C
1	Player	Hits	Runs
2	Carl	9	4
3	Amala	5	2
4	Doug	1	0
5	Noreen	11	5
6	David	3	3
7	Annina	2	1
8	Ted	7	3
9	Raoul	12	7
10	Cheryl	3	0
11			
12	Total	53	25

Carl made 9 hits and scored 4 runs. His name is in Cell A2, the number 9 is in Cell B2, and the number 4 is in Cell C2.

Think of a cell name as a variable. As the team plays more games, Carl will probably make more hits and score more runs, and the numbers in Cells B2 and C2 will change.

The total number of hits, 53, in Cell B12 is the following sum:

$$53 = 9 + 5 + 1 + 11 + 3 + 2 + 7 + 12 + 3$$

This is a special case of a formula that can be written using the cell names.

$$B12 = B2 + B3 + B4 + B5 + B6 + B7 + B8 + B9 + B10$$

1. a. What is in Cell A5? _____   b. What is in Cell B3? _____

2. a. Which cell contains the word "Runs"? _____

   b. Which cell contains the number 12? _____

   c. Which cell contains the total number of runs scored by all of the players? _____

3. Write a formula for calculating C12 that uses the cell names.

   _____

4. Suppose Raoul scored only 4 runs instead of 7. Which cell entries should be changed, and what should they be changed to?

   _____

Use with Lesson 3.7.

Spreadsheet Scramble Game Mats

	A	B	C	D	E	F
1						Total
2						
3						
4						
5	Total					

	A	B	C	D	E	F
1						Total
2						
3						
4						
5	Total					

	A	B	C	D	E	F
1						Total
2						
3						
4						
5	Total					

	A	B	C	D	E	F
1						Total
2						
3						
4						
5	Total					

	A	B	C	D	E	F
1						Total
2						
3						
4						
5	Total					

	A	B	C	D	E	F
1						Total
2						
3						
4						
5	Total					

	A	B	C	D	E	F
1						Total
2						
3						
4						
5	Total					

	A	B	C	D	E	F
1						Total
2						
3						
4						
5	Total					

Use with Lesson 3.7.

Date _____ Time _____

Mixed Practice

Rename each mixed number as a fraction.

1. $1\frac{3}{4}$ _____

2. $3\frac{1}{3}$ _____

3. $10\frac{1}{10}$ _____

4. $1\frac{2}{3}$ _____

5. $2\frac{2}{5}$ _____

6. $4\frac{5}{6}$ _____

7. $1\frac{1}{8}$ _____

8. $6\frac{2}{3}$ _____

Rename each fraction as a mixed or whole number.

9. $\frac{8}{3}$ _____

10. $\frac{17}{4}$ _____

11. $\frac{22}{5}$ _____

12. $\frac{45}{9}$ _____

13. $\frac{9}{5}$ _____

14. $\frac{6}{3}$ _____

15. $\frac{7}{2}$ _____

16. $\frac{11}{8}$ _____

Find at least the first six multiples of each number and then the least common multiple of each pair.

17. 7 _____

4 _____

Least common multiple _____

18. 3 _____

6 _____

Least common multiple _____

19. 8 _____

12 _____

Least common multiple _____

20. 5 _____

9 _____

Least common multiple _____

Use with Lesson 3.7.

Math Boxes 3.7

---

1. Rename each fraction as an equivalent fraction.

a. $\frac{1}{8} =$ _____

b. $\frac{3}{7} =$ _____

c. $\frac{8}{12} =$ _____

d. $\frac{4}{6} =$ _____

e. $\frac{6}{10} =$ _____

---

2. Divide. Do not use a calculator.

$12\overline{)70.8}$

---

3. The relationship between Ann's and Burt's weekly allowance is expressed by the formula $A = 2 * B$, where A stands for Ann's allowance and B for Burt's allowance.

a. If $B = \$5.00$, $A =$ _____.

b. If $A = \$5.00$, $B =$ _____.

c. If $B = \$4.50$, $A =$ _____.

---

4. Write in standard notation.

a. $7^6 =$ _____

b. $8^5 =$ _____

c. $5 * 10^7 =$ _____

d. $6 * 10^2 =$ _____

---

5. Give three special cases for the general pattern $\frac{a}{a} = 2 - \frac{a}{a}$.

_____

_____

_____

---

6. In 5 years, Gina will be twice as old as Scottie. Scottie is 8 years old now.

a. How old will Gina be in 5 years?

_____

b. How old is Gina now?

_____

Spreadsheet Practice

Students are selling coupon books to raise money for the school band. A coupon book sells for $2.50. When the spreadsheet at the right is completed, it will show how many books these four students sold and how much money they collected.

	A	B	C
1	Student	Books	Money
2	Luigi	5	$12.50
3	Robin	16	
4	Akira	30	
5	Gloria	13	
6	**Total**		

1. Fill in Cell B6 to show the total number of books sold.

2. Fill in Cells C3, C4, and C5 to show how much money Robin, Akira, and Gloria collected.

3. Fill in Cell C6 to show the total amount of money collected.

The spreadsheet below shows students' test scores for two different tests.

	A	B	C	D
1	Student	Test 1	Test 2	Average
2	Amy	85	90	87.5
3	David	70	86	
4	Amit	78	64	
5	Beth	65	81	

4. Calculate the remaining average test scores. Fill in the spreadsheet.

5. David's Test 1 score is in which cell? _____

6. The lowest test score shown is in Cell _____.

7. Circle the correct formula for calculating Beth's average score.

   D4 = (B4 + C4) / 2   D5 = B5 + C5   D5 = (B5 + C5) / 2

How Far Can You See?

Suppose you are outdoors in a flat place where your view is not
blocked by buildings or trees. You can see objects at ground level
for several miles. The higher you are above ground or water level,
the farther you can see. The distance you can see along Earth's
surface is limited because Earth is curved. The **horizon**—where
Earth and sky appear to intersect—is the farthest you can see along
Earth's surface.

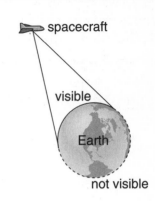

The formula $D = 1.25 * \sqrt{H}$ gives the approximate distance D in
miles you can see on a clear day. H is the height of your eyes
above ground or water level, measured in feet.

Reminder: $\sqrt{}$ means "**square root** of." For example, 2 is the square root of 4 ($\sqrt{4}$),
because $2 * 2 = 4$.

1. You are standing on a boat deck. Your eyes are 15 feet
   above water level. As you look across the water, about how
   far can you see? (Round to the nearest mile.)

   The distance is about _____ miles.

2. Use the formula to fill in the table. Calculate the distance to the nearest tenth of a
   mile. Then add two more locations and calculate the distances. Use a reference
   book to find the heights of interesting places.

Place	Height	Distance
Observation deck, Eiffel Tower, Paris, France	900 feet	About _____ miles
Top of Sears Tower, Chicago, Illinois, U.S.A.	1,454 feet	About _____ miles
Airplane	30,000 feet	About _____ miles
		About _____ miles
		About _____ miles

Challenge

3. If you see the horizon about 10 miles away, your eye is about _____
   above ground level.   (unit)

Math Boxes 3.8

1. Name the greatest common factor of each pair of numbers.

   a. 12 and 18 _____

   b. 21 and 7 _____

   c. 40 and 15 _____

   d. 13 and 16 _____

2. Solve.

   a. $7 + (-12) =$ _____

   b. $-8 + 8 =$ _____

   c. $-2 + (-10) =$ _____

   d. $-2 + 13 =$ _____

3. The spreadsheet below shows the number of baskets and free throws scored by players on a basketball team. Each basket is worth 2 points, and each free throw is worth 1 point.

	A	B	C	D
1	Player	Baskets	Free Throws	Total Points
2	Joe	3	3	9
3	Dion	1	2	
4	Fran	5	0	
5	Sam	8	4	
6	Mike	4	3	
7	Total			

   a. Complete the spreadsheet.

   b. What is shown in Cell B4? _____

   c. The greatest number of total points scored by a player is shown in Cell _____.

   d. Circle the correct formula for calculating the number of points Sam scored.

   D5 = B5 + C5   D5 = (2 * B5) + C5   D5 = B5 + (2 * C5)

   e. Circle the formula you should *not* use to calculate the total number of points the team scored.

   D7 = B7 + C7   D7 = D2 + D3 + D4 + D5 + D6   D7 = (2 * B7) + C7

Reading Graphs

Example In Cuba, the life expectancy for men in 1953 was 58 years. **Life expectancy**
is the number of years an average person can expect to live.

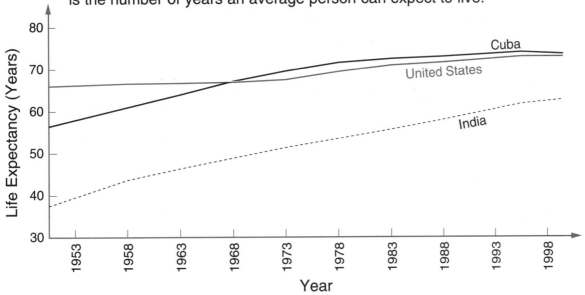

Sources: World Population Prospects: The 1992 Revision; The World Almanac
and Book of Facts 1996; and The World Almanac and Book of Facts 2000

1. In 1993, what was the life expectancy for men in Cuba? About _____
   (unit)

   In the United States? About _____   In India? About _____
   (unit)   (unit)

2. Mark the point on the graph at which life expectancy
   for men in Cuba overtakes life expectancy for men
   in the United States. About what year was that?

   _____

**Size of a Harvester Ant Colony
as the Colony Ages**

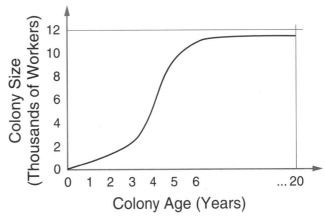

3. Mark the point on the graph at
   which life expectancy for men in
   India first reached 50 years.
   About what year was that? _____

   The graph at the right shows how the
   size of a harvester ant colony increases.

4. Estimate the size of the
   ant colony after three years. _____
   (unit)

   Source: American Scientist

5. The ant colony stops
   growing in size after about _____.
   (unit)

6. The number of ants in a colony that has stopped growing is about _____.
   (unit)

Time Graphs

1. Mr. Olds drove his son Hank to school. The trip from home to school took
   13 minutes. The graph below shows the speed that Mr. Olds traveled as he drove.
   Write a story that explains the shape of the graph.

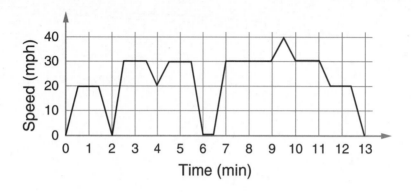

_____

_____

_____

_____

_____

2. Monica filled a cup with cocoa. She drank almost half of it. She refilled the cup.
   Then she drank all of the cocoa in the cup. Draw a graph that illustrates this story.

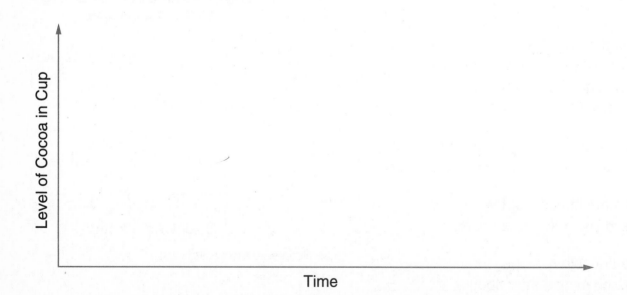

116

Mystery Graphs

Each of the following graphs represents one of the situations described below. Match each situation with its graph.

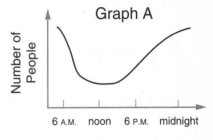

1. The number of people at a school is best described by Graph _____.

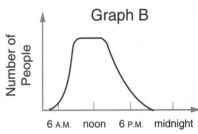

2. The number of people in a restaurant is best described by Graph _____.

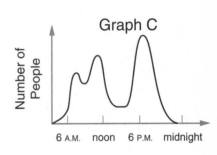

3. The number of people who are at home is best described by Graph _____.

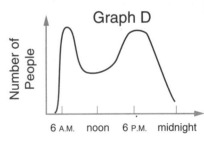

4. The number of people in a hospital is best described by Graph _____.

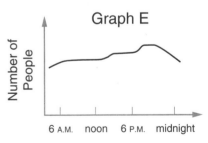

5. The number of people driving a car is best described by Graph _____.

6. For one of the situations above, explain why you chose to match that situation with a particular graph.

_____

_____

_____

Math Boxes 3.9

1. a. Name the least common multiple of

3, 4, and 8. _____

b. Name the least common multiple of

2, 5, and 6. _____

c. Name the least common multiple of

3, 4, and 5. _____

2. Multiply. Do not use a calculator.

_____ = 6.4 $*$ 5.8

3. Complete the table. Then graph the data and connect the points.

Harry travels about 8 miles per hour on his bike.

Rule: Distance traveled = 8 $*$ number of hours

Time (hr) (h)	Distance (mi) (8 $*$ h)
1	
2	
	24
5	
	56

4. The perimeter p of a rectangle can be found by the formula $p = 2 * (b + h)$.

a. Find the perimeter if b = 9 inches and h = 6 inches. _____
(unit)

b. Find the perimeter if b = 3.25 cm and h = 5.5 cm. _____
(unit)

5. Give three special cases for the general pattern $f + m^2 = f + m * m$.

_____

_____

_____

Math Boxes 3.10

---

1. Name the greatest common factor of each pair of numbers.

a. 16 and 20 _____

b. 9 and 36 _____

c. 50 and 20 _____

d. 18 and 7 _____

2. Add.

a. $9 + (-4) =$ _____

b. $15 + (-15) =$ _____

c. $-12 + (-7) =$ _____

d. $-5 + 13 =$ _____

---

3. Darin charges $3 an hour to baby-sit on weekdays and $4 an hour on weekends. The spreadsheet below is a record of the baby-sitting he did in a week.

	A	B	C
1	Day of the Week	Number of Hours	Earnings
2	Monday	4	
3	Wednesday	2	
4	Saturday	3	
5	Sunday	5	
6	Total		

a. Fill in the missing numbers on the spreadsheet.

b. What is shown in Cell B4? _____

c. The least number of hours he baby-sat is shown in Cell _____.

d. Circle the correct formula for calculating Darin's earnings on Wednesday.

   C3 = 2 * C2   C3 = 3 * B3   C3 = 4 * C2

e. Circle the formula Darin should *not* use to calculate his total earnings.

   C6 = C2 + C3 + C4 + C5   C6 = 3.5 * B6

   C6 = (3 * B2) + (3 * B3) + (4 * B4) + (4 * B5)

Formulas, Tables, and Graphs

Math Message

Imagine an ideal summer job, one that might actually exist. Describe what it would be. How often would you work? How much money do you think you could make by the end of the summer?

_____

_____

_____

Haylee and Chloe want to earn money during summer vacation.

- Haylee is going to cut lawns. Her father will lend her $190 to buy a lawn mower. She figures that she can cut 10 lawns per week and make $12 per lawn, after paying for oil and gasoline.

- Chloe is going to work in an ice cream shop. The owner will provide a uniform free of charge and pay her $4.80 per hour. She will work $3\frac{1}{2}$ hours per day, 5 days per week.

1. Complete the table to show how much profit each girl will have made after 1 week, 2 weeks, 3 weeks, and so on. (Assume they do not have to pay taxes.)

2. Use the table to answer the following questions.

   a. Who will have made more money by the end of 5 weeks?

   _____

   b. How much money will that girl have made?

   _____

   c. Who will make more money during the summer?

   _____

Time (weeks)	Profit (dollars)	
	Haylee	Chloe
Start	−190	0
1	−70	84
2		
3		
4		
5		
6	530	
7		
8		672
9		
10		

Use with Lesson 3.10.

Formulas, Tables, and Graphs (cont.)

3. Use the grid below to graph the profits from Haylee's and Chloe's summer jobs. Label the lines "Haylee" and "Chloe."

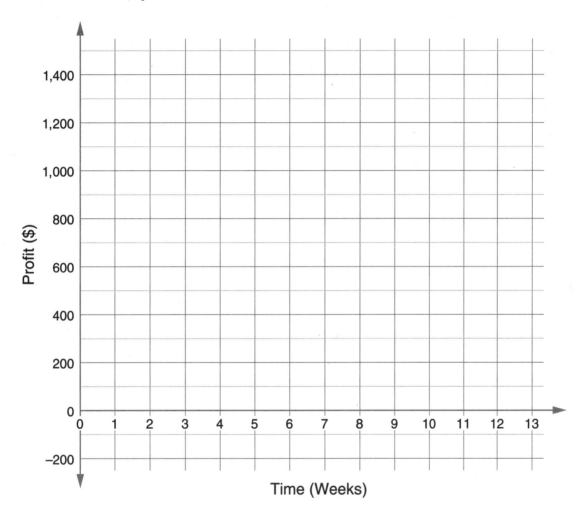

4. After 5 weeks, what will be the difference between the two girls' profits?

_____

5. Suppose that summer vacation is 13 weeks long instead of 10 weeks.

a. Who will make more money by the end of the summer?

_____

b. After 13 weeks, what will be the difference between the two girls' profits?

_____

Time to Reflect

1. The word *variable* often refers to a symbol in an algebraic expression, table, or formula. Can you think of ways the word *variable* is used that have nothing to do with mathematics? Give examples of such uses.

_____
_____
_____
_____
_____

2. Pablo said, "The formula for the area of a square can be written as $Q = k * k$ or $Q = k^2$. Q stands for area, and k stands for the length of a side."

   Is he correct? Explain.

_____
_____
_____
_____
_____

3. Which idea or activity did you especially like, or which activity did you not enjoy in this unit? Explain.

_____
_____
_____
_____
_____

Use with Lesson 3.11.

Math Boxes 3.11

---

1. Rename each fraction as a mixed number or a whole number.

   a. $\frac{7}{3}$ = _____

   b. $\frac{8}{4}$ = _____

   c. $\frac{9}{8}$ = _____

   d. $\frac{6}{6}$ = _____

   e. $\frac{12}{5}$ = _____

2. Name the greatest common factor of each pair of numbers.

   a. 30 and 18 _____

   b. 8 and 24 _____

   c. 60 and 25 _____

   d. 23 and 26 _____

---

3. Rename each fraction as an equivalent fraction.

   a. $\frac{3}{8}$ = _____

   b. $\frac{5}{7}$ = _____

   c. $\frac{6}{9}$ = _____

   d. $\frac{15}{20}$ = _____

   e. $\frac{8}{10}$ = _____

4. a. Name the least common multiple of 3, 4, and 6. _____

   b. Name the least common multiple of 2, 4, and 7. _____

   c. Name the least common multiple of 3, 4, and 8. _____

---

5. Mark and label the following numbers on the number line.

   a. $\frac{1}{4}$

   b. $1\frac{1}{9}$

   c. $\frac{12}{4}$

   d. $2\frac{3}{4}$

   e. $\frac{1}{2}$

Modeling Equivalent Fractions

Math Message

1. Fold a sheet of paper into 3 equal parts.
   Unfold it and color 2 of the parts. What fraction of the paper is colored? _____

   _____

2. Fold the paper back into thirds. Without unfolding it, fold it in half the other way.
   Fold it in half again.

   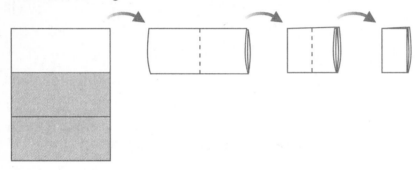

   a. How many rectangles are there? _____ rectangles

   b. How many are colored? _____ rectangles
      $\frac{8}{12}$ of the paper is colored. $\frac{2}{3}$ and $\frac{8}{12}$ are **equivalent fractions.**

3. Use paper folding to find a fraction equivalent to $\frac{3}{4}$.

   a. Fold a sheet of paper into 4 equal parts. Unfold it and
      color 3 of the parts. What fraction of the paper is colored? _____

   b. Draw a picture of the sheet of paper
      that shows $\frac{3}{4}$ colored.

   c. Fold the paper to create an
      equivalent fraction.

   d. Draw a picture of the paper that shows
      the equivalent fraction you made.

   e. How many equal parts are there? _____ equal parts

   f. How many parts are colored? _____ parts

   g. Name the equivalent fraction. _____

Use with Lesson 4.1.

Equivalent Fractions

You can find equivalent fractions in the following ways:

Multiplication Rule	Division Rule
To find an equivalent fraction, *multiply* the numerator and the denominator of the original fraction by the same (non-zero) number.	To find an equivalent fraction, *divide* the numerator and the denominator of the original fraction by the same (non-zero) number.
Example $\dfrac{2}{3}$: $\dfrac{2 * 2}{3 * 2} = \dfrac{4}{6}$	*Example* $\dfrac{20}{12}$: $\dfrac{20 \div 4}{12 \div 4} = \dfrac{5}{3}$

1. Find an equivalent fraction by multiplying.

    a. $\dfrac{3}{5}$ _____

    b. $\dfrac{5}{3}$ _____

    c. $\dfrac{3}{10}$ _____

    d. $\dfrac{3}{4}$ _____

    e. $\dfrac{2}{5}$ _____

2. Find an equivalent fraction by dividing.

    a. $\dfrac{6}{8}$ _____

    b. $\dfrac{8}{12}$ _____

    c. $\dfrac{50}{75}$ _____

    d. $\dfrac{30}{100}$ _____

    e. $\dfrac{36}{24}$ _____

3. Write three equivalent fractions for each given fraction.

    a. $\dfrac{2}{3}$ _____

    b. $\dfrac{5}{10}$ _____

    c. $\dfrac{5}{8}$ _____

    d. $\dfrac{50}{45}$ _____

    e. $\dfrac{45}{50}$ _____

    f. $\dfrac{16}{28}$ _____

4. Any whole number can be written as a fraction. For example: $2 = \dfrac{4}{2} = \dfrac{6}{3} = \dfrac{8}{4}$. Write at least two equivalent fractions for each whole number.

    a. 3 _____

    b. 4 _____

    c. 0 _____

    d. 1 _____

Equivalent Fractions (cont.)

A fraction is in **simplest form** if its numerator and denominator do not have any factors in common except 1.

For example, $\frac{2}{3}$ is in simplest form because the only **common factor** of 2 and 3 is 1. $\frac{4}{8}$ is not in simplest form, because 4 is a common factor of 4 and 8.

5. Circle the fractions that are in simplest form.

a. $\frac{3}{5}$ b. $\frac{4}{6}$ c. $\frac{9}{14}$ d. $\frac{12}{13}$ e. $\frac{12}{15}$ f. $\frac{8}{18}$

6. One way to find the simplest form of a fraction is to divide the numerator and denominator of the fraction by its **greatest common factor.**

Example 1
Rename $\frac{8}{12}$ as a fraction in simplest form. $\frac{8}{12} = \frac{8 \div 4}{12 \div 4} = \frac{2}{3}$
The greatest common factor of 8 and 12 is 4.

Write each fraction in simplest form.

a. $\frac{12}{16} = $ _____   b. $\frac{3}{9} = $ _____   c. $\frac{8}{14} = $ _____   d. $\frac{9}{15} = $ _____

e. $\frac{18}{45} = $ _____   f. $\frac{24}{32} = $ _____   g. $\frac{9}{24} = $ _____   h. $\frac{20}{25} = $ _____

7. Find the missing numbers.

Example 2 $\frac{3}{4} = \frac{x}{8}$

The denominator of the second fraction is twice as much as the denominator of the first fraction. Therefore, the numerator of the second fraction must also be twice as much as the numerator of the first fraction.

$\frac{3}{4} = \frac{3 * 2}{4 * 2} = \frac{6}{8}$; $x = 6$

Example 3 $\frac{9}{15} = \frac{3}{y}$

The numerator of the second fraction is one-third as much as the numerator of the first fraction. Therefore, the denominator of the second fraction must also be one-third as much as the denominator of the first fraction.

$\frac{9}{15} = \frac{9 \div 3}{15 \div 3} = \frac{3}{5}$; $y = 5$

a. $\frac{1}{4} = \frac{3}{y}$ $y = $ _____   b. $\frac{3}{z} = \frac{30}{50}$ $z = $ _____   c. $\frac{w}{8} = \frac{24}{32}$ $w = $ _____

d. $\frac{2}{3} = \frac{10}{x}$ $x = $ _____   e. $\frac{d}{4} = \frac{18}{24}$ $d = $ _____   f. $\frac{15}{25} = \frac{r}{5}$ $r = $ _____

Math Boxes 4.1

---

1. Tell whether each angle is an acute, right, obtuse, reflex, or straight angle.

a. 120° angle _____

b. 300° angle _____

c. 90° angle _____

d. 180° angle _____

SRB
148

---

2. Divide.

$$8\overline{)340.8}$$

SRB
50–53

---

3. Which graph best represents the number of inches an average adult grows during a year?

Graph _____

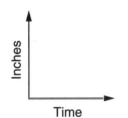
a.

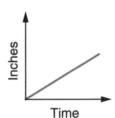
b.

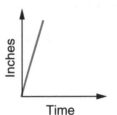
c.

SRB
134

---

4. Find the mean, median, mode, and range for the following set of numbers:

15, 31, 26, 28, 19, 22

mean _____

median _____

mode _____

range _____

SRB
130 131

---

5. Add.

a. 24 + (−8) = _____

b. 19 + (−26) = _____

c. −34 + (−18) = _____

d. −21 + 12 = _____

SRB
92 93

Comparing Fractions

Math Message

You can make any fraction out of the digits 0, 1, 2, 3, 4, 5, 6, 7, 8, and 9. The fraction $\frac{3}{4}$ is made up of two digits; the fraction $\frac{23}{6}$ is made up of three digits. A fraction may *not* have a denominator of 0.

Use only two digits to make the following fractions.

1. The smallest possible fraction that is greater than 0 _____

2. The largest possible fraction _____

3. The largest possible fraction that is less than 1 _____

4. The smallest possible fraction that is greater than $\frac{1}{2}$ _____

Compare each pair of fractions by first renaming them with a common denominator.

Write <, >, or =. Show how you got each answer.

Example $\frac{3}{4}$ _____ $\frac{5}{6}$

One way: The QCD is 4 * 6 = 24. Rename each fraction so that the denominator is 24.	Another way: The LCD of 4 and 6 is 12. Rename each fraction so that the denominator is 12.
$\frac{3}{4} = \frac{x}{24}$; $x = 18$ $\qquad$ $\frac{5}{6} = \frac{y}{24}$; $y = 20$ So $\frac{3}{4} = \frac{18}{24}$ $\qquad$ So $\frac{5}{6} = \frac{20}{24}$ Since $\frac{18}{24} < \frac{20}{24}$, then $\frac{3}{4} < \frac{5}{6}$	$\frac{3}{4} = \frac{x}{12}$; $x = 9$ $\qquad$ $\frac{5}{6} = \frac{x}{12}$; $x = 10$ So $\frac{3}{4} = \frac{9}{12}$ $\qquad$ So $\frac{5}{6} = \frac{10}{12}$ Since $\frac{9}{12} < \frac{10}{12}$, then $\frac{3}{4} < \frac{5}{6}$

5. $\frac{2}{3}$ _____ $\frac{4}{5}$

6. $\frac{2}{5}$ _____ $\frac{3}{10}$

7. $\frac{1}{3}$ _____ $\frac{5}{8}$

8. $\frac{2}{6}$ _____ $\frac{1}{5}$

9. $\frac{3}{4}$ _____ $\frac{18}{24}$

10. $\frac{7}{6}$ _____ $\frac{11}{9}$

Math Boxes 4.2

1. The table below shows the results of a survey in which pediatricians were asked to name their favorite way of treating their own children's coughs and colds. Use the Percent Circle to make a circle graph of the results.

Treatment	Percent of Pediatricians
Do nothing	62%
Rest and fluids	17%
Medicine	13%
Other	8%

Treating Children's Colds

SRB
139 140

---

2. Multiply.

$2.9 * 51 =$ _____

SRB
45 46

3. Write 5 fractions equivalent to $\frac{3}{5}$.

a. _____

b. _____

c. _____

d. _____

e. _____

SRB
68

---

4. Write each fraction in simplest form.

a. $\frac{3}{12} =$ _____

b. $\frac{5}{10} =$ _____

c. $\frac{6}{8} =$ _____

d. $\frac{8}{12} =$ _____

e. $\frac{3}{9} =$ _____

SRB
69

5. Add or subtract.

a. $\frac{1}{3} + \frac{4}{3} =$ _____

b. $\frac{1}{2} + \frac{1}{3} =$ _____

c. $\frac{1}{3} - \frac{1}{8} =$ _____

d. $\frac{6}{5} - \frac{1}{3} =$ _____

SRB
78

Fractions of a Square

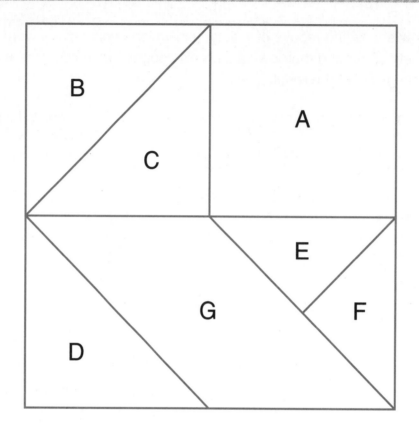

1. What fraction of the large square is ...

   a. Square A? _____

   b. Triangle B? _____

   c. Triangle E? _____

   d. Parallelogram G? _____

2. What fraction of the large square are the following pieces, when put together? Write a number model to show your answer.

   a. Triangles B and C _____

   b. Triangles E and F _____

   c. Square A and Triangle C _____

   d. Square A and Triangle E _____

   e. Triangles E and B _____

   f. Square A and Parallelogram G _____

   g. Triangles D, E, and F and Parallelogram G _____

   _____

Use with Lesson 4.3.

Adding and Subtracting Fractions

To add or subtract fractions with different denominators, first find equivalent fractions with a common denominator. Then simply add or subtract the numerators.

Examples $\frac{1}{8} + \frac{3}{8} = \frac{1+3}{8} = \frac{4}{8} = \frac{1}{2}$ | $\frac{2}{3} - \frac{1}{4} = \frac{8}{12} - \frac{3}{12} = \frac{8-3}{12} = \frac{5}{12}$

Add or subtract. Write your answers as fractions in simplest form.

1. $\frac{1}{2} + \frac{1}{4} =$ _____

2. $\frac{1}{3} + \frac{1}{2} =$ _____

3. $1 - \frac{1}{4} =$ _____

4. $\frac{1}{2} + \frac{1}{6} =$ _____

5. $\frac{3}{4} - \frac{1}{6} =$ _____

6. $\frac{5}{6} + \frac{1}{12} =$ _____

7. $\frac{1}{8} + \frac{1}{4} =$ _____

8. $\frac{2}{3} + \frac{5}{6} =$ _____

9. $\frac{1}{3} + \frac{1}{6} - \frac{2}{12} =$ _____

For each of the following, first estimate whether the sum is greater than 1 or less than 1. Then calculate the sum and check your estimate.

	> 1 or < 1	Sum			> 1 or < 1	Sum
10. $\frac{3}{4} + \frac{3}{8}$	_____	_____		**11.** $\frac{1}{2} + \frac{2}{3}$	_____	_____
12. $\frac{3}{5} + \frac{1}{10}$	_____	_____		**13.** $\frac{1}{8} + \frac{1}{5}$	_____	_____

14. Mentally estimate the sums and differences below. Write the letter of the problem by the point on the number line closest to your estimate. Study 14a. as an example.

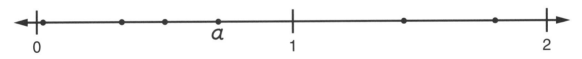

a. $\frac{3}{8} + \frac{1}{3}$

b. $\frac{7}{8} + \frac{12}{13}$

c. $\frac{9}{10} - \frac{7}{8}$

d. $\frac{1}{3} + \frac{1}{6}$

e. $\frac{5}{6} + \frac{3}{5}$

f. $\frac{7}{12} - \frac{1}{4}$

15. Name two fractions that have a sum

a. between 1 and 2.

b. between $\frac{1}{2}$ and 1.

c. between $\frac{1}{2}$ and $\frac{3}{4}$.

_____

_____

_____

1. Tell whether each angle is an acute, right, obtuse, reflex, or straight angle.

    a. 270° angle _____

    b. 10° angle _____

    c. 130° angle _____

    d. $40\frac{1}{2}°$ angle _____

2. Divide.

    $6\overline{)352.2}$

3. Which graph best represents the number of phone calls an average person makes during a day?

    Graph _____

    a.
    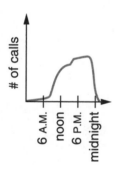

    b.
    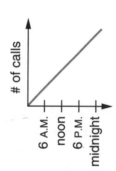

    c.
    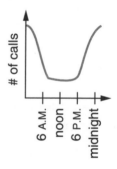

4. Find the mean, median, mode, and range for the following set of numbers:

    86, 91, 83, 94, 83, 88

    mean _____

    median _____

    mode _____

    range _____

5. Add.

    a. 46 + (−13) = _____

    b. 25 + (−76) = _____

    c. −27 + (−44) = _____

    d. −46 + 37 = _____

Use with Lesson 4.3.

Math Boxes 4.4

1. The table below shows the results of a survey of people's favorite Olympic sports. Use the Percent Circle to make a circle graph of the results.

Favorite Sport	Percent of People
Gymnastics	35%
Swimming	15%
Basketball	40%
Other	10%

Olympic Sports Preferences

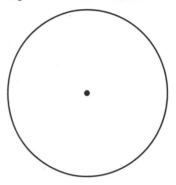

2. Multiply.

   $34 * 0.67 = $ _____

3. Write 5 fractions equivalent to $\frac{3}{8}$.

   a. _____

   b. _____

   c. _____

   d. _____

   e. _____

4. Write each fraction in its simplest form.

   a. $\frac{9}{12} = $ _____

   b. $\frac{2}{8} = $ _____

   c. $\frac{10}{15} = $ _____

   d. $\frac{15}{18} = $ _____

   e. $\frac{15}{24} = $ _____

5. Add or subtract.

   a. $\frac{1}{4} + \frac{3}{4} = $ _____

   b. $\frac{5}{6} + \frac{2}{3} = $ _____

   c. $1 - \frac{3}{7} = $ _____

   d. $\frac{8}{5} - \frac{7}{10} = $ _____

Adding and Subtracting Mixed Numbers

Example 1 $1\frac{2}{5} + 2\frac{4}{5} = ?$

| **Step 1**
 Add the fractions. Then add the whole numbers.

 $\begin{array}{r} 1\frac{2}{5} \\ +\ 2\frac{4}{5} \\ \hline 3\frac{6}{5} \end{array}$ | **Step 2**
 If necessary, rename the sum.

 $3\frac{6}{5} = 3 + \frac{6}{5}$
 $= 3 + \frac{5}{5} + \frac{1}{5}$
 $= 3 + 1 + \frac{1}{5}$
 $= 4\frac{1}{5}$ |

Add. Write your answers in simplest form.

1. $\begin{array}{r} 4\frac{1}{5} \\ +\ 3\frac{2}{5} \\ \hline \end{array}$ 2. $\begin{array}{r} 1\frac{2}{4} \\ +\ 2\frac{3}{4} \\ \hline \end{array}$ 3. $\begin{array}{r} 5\frac{1}{4} \\ +\ 1\frac{3}{4} \\ \hline \end{array}$ 4. $\begin{array}{r} 1\frac{4}{8} \\ +\ 1\frac{2}{8} \\ \hline \end{array}$

Example 2 $4\frac{5}{8} - 2\frac{1}{8} = ?$

| **Step 1**
 Subtract the fractions.
 Then subtract the whole numbers.

 $\begin{array}{r} 4\frac{5}{8} \\ -\ 2\frac{1}{8} \\ \hline 2\frac{4}{8} \end{array}$ | **Step 2**
 If necessary, rename the difference.

 $\begin{array}{r} 4\frac{5}{8} \\ -\ 2\frac{1}{8} \\ \hline 2\frac{4}{8} = 2\frac{1}{2} \end{array}$ |

Example 3 $5\frac{1}{3} - 1\frac{2}{3} = ?$

Notice that the fraction in the first mixed number is less than the fraction in the second mixed number. Since $\frac{2}{3}$ can't be subtracted from $\frac{1}{3}$, you need to rename $5\frac{1}{3}$.

| **Step 1**
 Rename the first mixed number.

 $5\frac{1}{3} = 4 + 1 + \frac{1}{3}$
 $= 4 + \frac{3}{3} + \frac{1}{3}$
 $= 4 + \frac{4}{3} = 4\frac{4}{3}$ | **Step 2**
 Subtract the fractions.
 Then subtract the whole numbers.

 $5\frac{1}{3} \longrightarrow 4\frac{4}{3}$
 $\begin{array}{r} -1\frac{2}{3} \qquad\quad -1\frac{2}{3} \\ \hline 3\frac{2}{3} \end{array}$ |

Adding and Subtracting Mixed Numbers (cont.)

Example 4 $8 - 3\frac{5}{8} = ?$

Step 1	**Step 2**
Rename the whole number.	Subtract the fractions. Then subtract the whole numbers.

Step 1
Rename the whole number.

$$8 = 7 + 1$$
$$= 7 + \frac{8}{8}$$
$$= 7\frac{8}{8}$$

Step 2
Subtract the fractions. Then subtract the whole numbers.

$$8 \longrightarrow 7\frac{8}{8}$$
$$-3\frac{5}{8} \quad -3\frac{5}{8}$$
$$\overline{ 4\frac{3}{8}}$$

Add or subtract.

5. $3\frac{1}{4}$
    $-2\frac{3}{4}$

6. $4\frac{1}{5}$
    $-2\frac{2}{5}$

7. 5
    $-2\frac{2}{3}$

8. 7
    $-3\frac{1}{4}$

9. $4\frac{1}{6}$
    $+2\frac{1}{6}$

10. $3\frac{1}{5}$
    $-1\frac{3}{5}$

11. 5
    $-1\frac{3}{4}$

12. $6\frac{7}{8}$
    $+3\frac{3}{8}$

13. Joe has a board $8\frac{3}{4}$ inches long. He cuts off $1\frac{1}{4}$ inches. How long is the remaining piece? _____

14. Mr. Ventrelli is making bread. He adds $1\frac{1}{4}$ cups of white flour and $1\frac{1}{4}$ cups of wheat flour. The recipe calls for the same number of cups of water as cups of flour. How much water should he add?

_____

15. Evelyn's house is between Robert's and Elizabeth's. How far is Robert's house from Elizabeth's?

_____

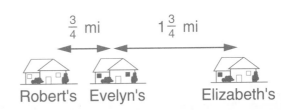

Robert's   Evelyn's   Elizabeth's

More Adding and Subtracting of Mixed Numbers

Fill in the missing numeral to rename the mixed number.

1. $\frac{5}{3} = 1\frac{\square}{3}$

2. $3\frac{7}{4} = 4\frac{\square}{4}$

3. $6\frac{12}{8} = \underline{\quad}\frac{4}{8}$

4. $5\frac{2}{5} = 4\frac{\square}{5}$

5. $8\frac{2}{3} = 7\frac{\square}{3}$

6. $2\frac{3}{8} = 1\frac{\square}{8}$

You can use what you know about adding and subtracting fractions to help you add and subtract mixed numbers with different denominators.

Example 1 $1\frac{1}{3} + 3\frac{5}{6} = ?$

Rename $\frac{1}{3}$ as $\frac{2}{6}$.
Then add.

$$1\frac{1}{3} \longrightarrow 1\frac{2}{6}$$
$$+\ 3\frac{5}{6} \qquad\quad +\ 3\frac{5}{6}$$
$$\overline{\qquad\qquad\qquad 4\frac{7}{6}} \longrightarrow 5\frac{1}{6}$$

Example 2 $8\frac{2}{5} - 2\frac{1}{2} = ?$

Rename $\frac{2}{5}$ as $\frac{4}{10}$ and $\frac{1}{2}$ as $\frac{5}{10}$.
Then rename $8\frac{4}{10}$ as $7\frac{14}{10}$. Subtract.

$$8\frac{2}{5} \longrightarrow 8\frac{4}{10} \longrightarrow 7\frac{14}{10}$$
$$-\ 2\frac{1}{2} \qquad\quad -\ 2\frac{5}{10} \qquad\quad -\ 2\frac{5}{10}$$
$$\overline{\qquad\qquad\qquad\qquad\qquad\qquad\quad 5\frac{9}{10}}$$

Add or subtract. Show your work.

7.
$$1\frac{3}{4}$$
$$+\ 3\frac{2}{8}$$

8.
$$3\frac{1}{2}$$
$$-\ 1\frac{1}{4}$$

9.
$$6$$
$$-\ 2\frac{1}{5}$$

10.
$$2\frac{7}{8}$$
$$+\ 1\frac{3}{4}$$

11. $6\frac{1}{8} - 5\frac{1}{4} = $ _____

12. $5\frac{1}{3} - 4\frac{3}{4} = $ _____

Use with Lesson 4.5.

More Adding and Subtracting of Mixed Numbers (cont.)

13. To check your answer to Problem 10, draw a line segment $2\frac{7}{8}$ inches long. Then, make it $1\frac{3}{4}$ inches longer.

Measure the whole line segment. How long is it? _____

14. Tim walked $\frac{1}{2}$ mile from school to the park. Then he walked $\frac{1}{4}$ mile to the store to get milk and orange juice. These items cost $2\frac{1}{2}$ dollars. Then he walked home, another $\frac{3}{4}$ of a mile.

How far did Tim walk in all? _____

Find a way to solve these problems without finding common denominators.
Write number models to show the order in which you added and subtracted.

15. $1\frac{1}{2} + 3\frac{7}{8} + 4\frac{1}{2} + 1\frac{1}{8} =$ _____

_____

16. $3\frac{1}{2} + 4\frac{2}{3} - 1\frac{1}{2} =$ _____

_____

17. If you drive $5\frac{4}{5}$ miles from Alphatown along Highway 1, you reach Betaville. Driving farther, you reach Gamma, which is $8\frac{1}{10}$ miles from Alphatown.

a. Mark the number line below to show the locations of Betaville and Gamma.

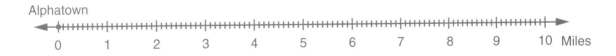

b. How far is it from Betaville to Gamma? _____

Water Problems

1. The largest ocean is the Pacific Ocean. Its area is 64 million square miles. The second largest ocean is the Atlantic Ocean. Let P stand for the area of the Pacific Ocean. If $P - 30.6$ stands for the area of the Atlantic, then what is the area of the Atlantic?

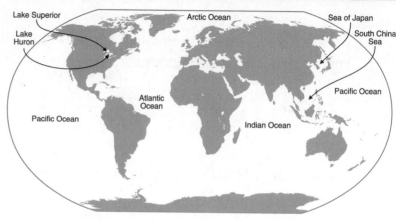

_____
                (unit)

2. The third largest ocean is the Indian Ocean. Its area is 28.3 million square miles. Write an algebraic expression using P that represents the area of the Indian Ocean.

_____

3. The fourth largest ocean is the Arctic Ocean. If $\frac{P}{12}$ stands for the approximate area of the Arctic, then what is the approximate area of the Arctic?

_____
                (unit)

4. Let A stand for the area of the Arctic Ocean. The area of the South China Sea, the largest sea in the world, is about $\frac{1}{5}$ the area of the Arctic Ocean.

   a. Write an algebraic expression, using the variable A, to represent the area of the South China Sea.   _____

   b. What is the approximate area of the South China Sea?

_____
                (unit)

5. The deepest point in the Sea of Japan is 5,468 feet below sea level. The deepest point in the Indian Ocean is 7,534 feet deeper. How many feet below sea level is the deepest point in the Indian Ocean?

_____
                (unit)

6. The area of Lake Superior, the largest of the Great Lakes, is 31,699 square miles. The area of Lake Huron, the second largest, is 23,004 square miles. How much larger is Lake Superior than Lake Huron?

_____
                (unit)

                                        Use with Lesson 4.5.

Math Boxes 4.5

---

1. Draw and label the following angle.

∠POL 135°

SRB
212-214

2. Divide.

12)‾3‾0‾3‾.‾6‾1‾ .

SRB
50–53

---

3. Add or subtract. Write the answer as a mixed number in simplest form.

a. $3\frac{1}{4} + 1\frac{1}{4} =$ _____

b. $5\frac{2}{3} + \frac{2}{4} =$ _____

c. $2\frac{3}{4} - \frac{1}{4} =$ _____

d. $1\frac{2}{3} - 1\frac{1}{4} =$ _____

SRB
80–82

4. Write the following in standard notation.

a. _____ $= 3.67 * 10^4$

b. $45.2 * 10^{-4} =$ _____

c. $2.01 * 10^{-2} =$ _____

d. _____ $= 0.0443 * 10^6$

SRB
8

---

5. Rename each mixed number as a mixed number in simplest form.

a. $1\frac{17}{4} =$ _____

b. _____ $= 2\frac{13}{6}$

c. $3\frac{28}{5} =$ _____

d. $4\frac{36}{9} =$ _____

e. _____ $= 6\frac{43}{3}$

SRB
67

6. Multiply mentally.

a. $0.8 * 100 =$ _____

b. $0.03 * 10 =$ _____

c. _____ $= 0.27 * 1,000$

d. _____ $= 0.004 * 100$

e. $5.8 * 100 =$ _____

SRB
43 44

A Fraction Multiplication Algorithm

Math Message

1. Use the number line to help you solve the problems in Columns 1 and 2 below.
   Reminder: The word *of* often means *times*.

	Column 1	Column 2

Column 1

$\frac{1}{2}$ of 3 = _____

$\frac{1}{4}$ of $\frac{1}{2}$ = _____

$\frac{5}{8}$ of 1 = _____

$\frac{1}{3}$ of $\frac{3}{4}$ = _____

Column 2

$\frac{1}{2} * 3$ = _____

$\frac{1}{4} * \frac{1}{2}$ = _____

$\frac{5}{8} * 1$ = _____

$\frac{1}{3} * \frac{3}{4}$ = _____

2. How are the problems in Column 1 like their partner problems in Column 2?

   _____

   _____

3. Circle the general pattern(s) below that are true for the partner problems in Columns 1 and 2.

   $a + b = b + a$ $a * b = b * c$ a of $b = a * b$ $a \div b = b \div a$

Six special cases of a general pattern are given below. Write the answer in simplest form for each special case. Study the first one.

4. $\frac{1}{5} * \frac{2}{3} = \frac{1*2}{5*3} = \frac{2}{15}$

5. $\frac{3}{4} * \frac{1}{2} = \frac{3*1}{4*2} = $ _____

6. $\frac{2}{1} * \frac{2}{4} = \frac{2*2}{1*4} = $ _____

7. $\frac{2}{4} * \frac{3}{5} = \frac{2*3}{4*5} = $ _____

8. $\frac{4}{6} * \frac{1}{2} = \frac{4*1}{6*2} = $ _____

9. $\frac{3}{7} * \frac{1}{3} = \frac{3*1}{7*3} = $ _____

10. Describe the general pattern in words. (*Hint:* Look at the numerators and denominators of the factors and products.)

    _____

    _____

    _____

Use with Lesson 4.6.

A Fraction Multiplication Algorithm (cont.)

11. Try to write the general pattern for Problem 10 using variables.
    (*Hint:* Use four variables.)

    _____

Use the general pattern you found in Problem 11 to solve the following multiplication
problems. Study the first one.

12. $\frac{3}{8} * \frac{2}{3} =$ $\dfrac{3 * 2}{8 * 3} = \dfrac{6}{24}$

13. $\frac{1}{3} * \frac{2}{3} =$ _____

14. $\frac{4}{5} * \frac{2}{8} =$ _____

15. $\frac{3}{12} * \frac{2}{4} =$ _____

16. $\frac{3}{4} * \frac{5}{6} =$ _____

17. $\frac{7}{9} * \frac{3}{8} =$ _____

18. $\frac{2}{5} * \frac{7}{8} =$ _____

19. $\frac{5}{10} * \frac{4}{7} =$ _____

Write the following whole numbers as fractions. The first one has been done for you.

20. $6 = \dfrac{6}{1}$

21. $3 =$ _____

22. $5 =$ _____

23. $7 =$ _____

24. Rewrite the following problems as fraction multiplication problems and solve them.
    Study the first one.

    a. $4 * \frac{2}{3} = \dfrac{4}{1} * \dfrac{2}{3} = \dfrac{8}{3}$

    b. $6 * \frac{3}{5} =$ _____ $=$ _____

    c. $7 * \frac{5}{6} =$ _____ $=$ _____

    d. $3 * \frac{3}{4} =$ _____ $=$ _____

Challenge

25. Write a general pattern with variables for the special cases in Problem 24.
    (*Hint:* Use three variables.)

    _____

26. Mark took a timed multiplication test and finished $\frac{3}{4}$ of the problems.
    He correctly answered $\frac{1}{2}$ of the problems he finished. What fraction
    of the problems on the test did Mark do correctly?

    _____

Math Boxes 4.6

1. Measure the angle to the nearest degree.

Measure of ∠MOP is _____°.

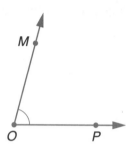

SRB
212–214

2. Compare. Write < or > .

a. $\frac{4}{9}$ _____ $\frac{3}{5}$

b. $\frac{3}{4}$ _____ $\frac{5}{8}$

c. $\frac{6}{7}$ _____ $\frac{4}{5}$

d. $\frac{1}{9}$ _____ $\frac{1}{10}$

SRB
70

3. Evaluate the following algebraic expressions for $b = \frac{1}{6}$.

a. $5\frac{2}{3} + b$ _____

b. $5 - b$ _____

c. $8 * b$ _____

d. $b - 2$ _____

SRB
223–225

4. Multiply. Write each answer in simplest form.

a. $\frac{1}{4} * \frac{3}{5} =$ _____

b. $\frac{1}{2} * \frac{7}{8} =$ _____

c. _____ $= \frac{3}{4} * \frac{5}{9}$

d. _____ $= \frac{2}{5} * \frac{4}{5}$

e. $\frac{7}{8} * \frac{1}{3} =$ _____

SRB
84 85

5. This spreadsheet shows the number of hours three students slept on two different nights.

a. Calculate the average number of hours of sleep for each student. Write these averages on the spreadsheet.

	A	B	C	D
1	Student	Monday	Tuesday	Average
2	Elaine	7.5	9	
3	Frank	6	10.5	
4	David	8	8.5	

b. Using cell names, write a formula for calculating David's average number of hours of sleep.

_____

SRB
136–138

Multiplying Mixed Numbers

Here are two methods for multiplying mixed numbers.

Example $3\frac{3}{4} * 2\frac{2}{3} = ?$

Partial–Products Method

$$3\frac{3}{4}$$
$$*\ 2\frac{2}{3}$$

$2 * 3 = 6$

$2 * \frac{3}{4} = \frac{6}{4} = 1\ \ \frac{1}{2}$

$\frac{2}{3} * 3 = \frac{6}{3} = 2$

$\frac{2}{3} * \frac{3}{4} = \frac{6}{12} = \ \ \ \frac{1}{2}$

$$9 + 1 = 10$$

$6 + 1 + 2$

$\frac{1}{2} + \frac{1}{2}$

Renaming–Mixed–Numbers Method

$3\frac{3}{4} * 2\frac{2}{3} = ?$

Rename the mixed numbers as fractions:

$3\frac{3}{4} = \frac{15}{4} \qquad 2\frac{2}{3} = \frac{8}{3}$

Multiply:

$\frac{15}{4} * \frac{8}{3} = \frac{15 * 8}{4 * 3} = \frac{120}{12}$

Rename the product:

$\frac{120}{12} = 10$

Multiply. Use one of the methods above or one of your own. Show your work.

1. $2\frac{3}{8} * \frac{1}{5} =$ _____

2. $3\frac{2}{5} * 2\frac{2}{3} =$ _____

3. $5\frac{3}{4} * 2\frac{5}{9} =$ _____

4. _____ $= 4\frac{6}{7} * \frac{3}{7}$

5. $4 * 6\frac{7}{10} =$ _____

6. $3\frac{11}{12} * 2\frac{1}{2} =$ _____

7. _____ $= 5\frac{7}{8} * 2\frac{1}{8}$

8. $4\frac{1}{6} * 3\frac{9}{4} =$ _____

Multiplying Mixed Numbers (cont.)

Find the area of each figure below.

Area of a rectangle $A = b * h$	Area of a triangle $A = \frac{1}{2} * b * h$	Area of a parallelogram $A = b * h$

9.

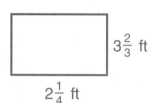

$3\frac{2}{3}$ ft

$2\frac{1}{4}$ ft

Area = _____
(unit)

10.

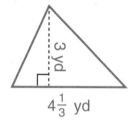

3 yd

$4\frac{1}{3}$ yd

Area = _____
(unit)

11.

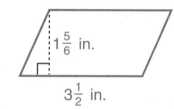

$1\frac{5}{6}$ in.

$3\frac{1}{2}$ in.

Area = _____
(unit)

12. Joan made a cubic box out of cardboard.
What is the area of all the cardboard she used?

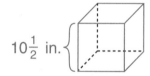

$10\frac{1}{2}$ in.

Area = _____
(unit)

Challenge

13. Lydia is putting photographs in an album. She does not like to leave more than $\frac{1}{3}$ of a page uncovered.

a. At the right are the dimensions of an album page and four photographs. If Lydia puts these four photographs on one page, what area of the page will be left uncovered?

_____
(unit)

b. Is this amount more or less than $\frac{1}{3}$ of the total area of the page?

_____

	Height	Width
Album page	$6\frac{3}{4}$"	9"
Photograph 1	$4\frac{1}{8}$"	$2\frac{1}{2}$"
Photograph 2	$3\frac{5}{8}$"	4"
Photograph 3	$2\frac{1}{8}$"	$2\frac{3}{4}$"
Photograph 4	$2\frac{1}{8}$"	$2\frac{1}{8}$"

Math Boxes 4.7

---

1. Draw and label the following angle.

$\angle MAL$ 64°

---

2. Divide.

$15\overline{)544.5}$

---

3. Add or subtract. Write the answer as a mixed number in simplest form.

a. $2\frac{1}{6} + 4\frac{3}{6} =$ _____

b. $4\frac{5}{6} - 2\frac{2}{3} =$ _____

c. $2\frac{1}{5} - \frac{3}{5} =$ _____

d. $5\frac{3}{4} - 3\frac{1}{8} =$ _____

---

4. Write the following in standard notation.

a. $5.4 * 10^3 =$ _____

b. $18 * 10^{-2} =$ _____

c. $0.078 * 10^5 =$ _____

d. _____ $= 44.35 * 10^{-3}$

---

5. Rename each mixed number as a mixed number in simplest form.

a. $2\frac{25}{3} =$ _____

b. _____ $= 1\frac{17}{5}$

c. $3\frac{46}{9} =$ _____

d. $2\frac{35}{7} =$ _____

e. _____ $= 1\frac{68}{8}$

---

6. Multiply mentally.

a. $0.2 * 100 =$ _____

b. $0.05 * 10 =$ _____

c. _____ $= 0.76 * 1,000$

d. _____ $= 0.009 * 100$

e. $36.4 * 100 =$ _____

Fractions, Decimals, and Percents

Math Message

During the baseball season, Sari got a hit
2 out of every 5 times she was at bat.

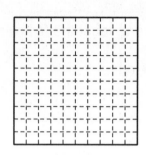

1. Shade $\frac{2}{5}$ of the square on the right.

2. How many hundredths are shaded? _____

3. $\frac{2}{5} = \frac{x}{100}$ $x =$ _____

You can rename some fractions as decimals by first renaming them as equivalent
fractions with 10 or 100 in the denominator.

> **Examples**
>
> $\frac{3}{5} = \frac{b}{10}$ $b = 6$ $\frac{3}{20} = \frac{d}{100}$ $d = 15$
>
> $\frac{6}{10} = 0.6$ $\frac{15}{100} = 0.15$
>
> So, $\frac{3}{5} = 0.6$ So, $\frac{3}{20} = 0.15$

Find the value of the variable. Use it to rename the fraction as a decimal.

4. $\frac{1}{4} = \frac{f}{100}$; $f =$ _____   5. $\frac{4}{5} = \frac{r}{100}$; $r =$ _____

  $\frac{1}{4} = 0.$ _____ $\frac{4}{5} = 0.$ _____

6. $\frac{7}{20} = \frac{z}{100}$; $z =$ _____   7. $\frac{9}{2} = \frac{n}{100}$; $n =$ _____

  $\frac{7}{20} = 0.$ _____ $\frac{9}{2} = 4.$ _____

Rename each fraction as a decimal.

8. $\frac{3}{4} = 0.$ _____   9. $\frac{12}{25} = 0.$ _____

10. $\frac{19}{50} = 0.$ _____   11. $\frac{3}{2} = 1.$ _____

Fractions, Decimals, and Percents (cont.)

Rename each decimal as a fraction in simplest form.

| **Examples** |
| $0.6 = \frac{6}{10} = \frac{3}{5}$ $\qquad$ $0.32 = \frac{32}{100} = \frac{8}{25}$ |

12. $0.5 =$ _____

13. $0.25 =$ _____

14. $0.4 =$ _____

15. $0.65 =$ _____

16. $0.75 =$ _____

17. $0.46 =$ _____

18. $0.89 =$ _____

19. $0.36 =$ _____

Rename each fraction as a percent.

| **Examples** |
| $\frac{2}{5} = \frac{40}{100} = 40\%$ $\qquad$ $\frac{9}{20} = \frac{45}{100} = 45\%$ |

20. $\frac{1}{4} = \dfrac{\boxed{}}{100} =$ ____%

21. $\frac{3}{5} = \dfrac{\boxed{}}{100} =$ ____%

22. $\frac{7}{10} = \dfrac{\boxed{}}{100} =$ ____%

23. $\frac{28}{50} = \dfrac{\boxed{}}{100} =$ ____%

24. $\frac{11}{20} = \dfrac{\boxed{}}{100} =$ ____%

25. $\frac{17}{25} = \dfrac{\boxed{}}{100} =$ ____%

26. $\frac{1}{20} = \dfrac{\boxed{}}{100} =$ ____%

27. $\frac{13}{10} = \dfrac{\boxed{}}{100} =$ ____%

Rename each percent as a fraction in simplest form.

| **Examples** |
| $40\% = \frac{40}{100} = \frac{2}{5}$ $\qquad$ $34\% = \frac{34}{100} = \frac{17}{50}$ |

28. $25\% = \dfrac{\boxed{}}{100} = \dfrac{\boxed{}}{4}$

29. $20\% = \dfrac{\boxed{}}{100} = \dfrac{\boxed{}}{5}$

30. $30\% = \dfrac{\boxed{}}{100} = \dfrac{\boxed{}}{10}$

31. $80\% = \dfrac{\boxed{}}{100} = \dfrac{\boxed{}}{5}$

32. $75\% = \dfrac{\boxed{}}{100} = \dfrac{\boxed{}}{4}$

33. $95\% = \dfrac{\boxed{}}{100} = \dfrac{\boxed{}}{20}$

34. $120\% = \dfrac{\boxed{}}{100} = \dfrac{\boxed{}}{5}$

35. $150\% = \dfrac{\boxed{}}{100} = \dfrac{\boxed{}}{2}$

Use with Lesson 4.8.

Adding or Subtracting Fractions and Mixed Numbers

Add or subtract. Write each answer in simplest terms. If possible, write answers as mixed numbers or whole numbers.

1. $\frac{5}{10} + \frac{3}{10} =$ _____

2. $\frac{7}{8} - \frac{3}{8} =$ _____

3. $\frac{3}{10} + \frac{4}{5} =$ _____

4. $\frac{3}{4} - \frac{2}{3} =$ _____

5. $3\frac{1}{12} + 2\frac{5}{12} =$ _____

6. $2\frac{5}{6} + 1\frac{4}{6} =$ _____

7. $4\frac{6}{8} - 3\frac{2}{8} =$ _____

8. $5\frac{1}{5} - 2\frac{3}{5} =$ _____

9. $8 - 6\frac{1}{3} =$ _____

10. $2\frac{1}{2} + 5\frac{1}{3} =$ _____

11. $1\frac{5}{6} - 1\frac{2}{3} =$ _____

12. $2\frac{1}{8} - 1\frac{1}{2} =$ _____

Use with Lesson 4.8.

Date _____   Time _____

---

1. Measure the angle to the nearest degree.

Measure of ∠*TAP* is _____°.

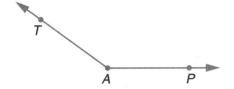

2. Compare. Write < or >.

a. $\frac{7}{3}$ _____ $\frac{3}{7}$

b. $\frac{5}{6}$ _____ $\frac{5}{7}$

c. $\frac{2}{3}$ _____ $\frac{4}{9}$

d. $\frac{5}{8}$ _____ $\frac{6}{13}$

---

3. Evaluate the following algebraic expressions for $k = \frac{3}{5}$.

a. $k + 2\frac{3}{10}$ _____

b. $7 - k$ _____

c. $k * 4$ _____

d. $k - 1$ _____

4. Multiply. Write each answer in simplest form.

a. $\frac{3}{8} * 6 =$ _____

b. $2\frac{1}{7} * \frac{4}{5} =$ _____

c. $\frac{8}{9} * 2\frac{1}{3} =$ _____

d. $\frac{7}{8} * \frac{9}{5} =$ _____

e. $6\frac{2}{3} * 3\frac{3}{4} =$ _____

---

5. This spreadsheet shows students' times, in seconds, for two different runs.

a. Calculate the average time for each student. Write these average times on the spreadsheet.

b. Using cell names, write a formula for calculating Jake's average time.

_____

	A	B	C	D
1	Student	Run 1	Run 2	Average
2	Jake	23	21	
3	Steve	20	19	
4	Allison	21.5	21	

Fractions, Decimals, and Percents

Math Message

Fill in the blanks.

1. $0.36 = \dfrac{0.36 * 100}{100} = \dfrac{\boxed{}}{100} =$ _____ %

2. $0.7 = \dfrac{0.7 * 100}{100} = \dfrac{\boxed{}}{100} =$ _____ %

3. $0.09 = \dfrac{0.09 * 100}{100} = \dfrac{\boxed{}}{100} =$ _____ %

4. $4.602 = \dfrac{4.602 * 100}{100} = \dfrac{\boxed{}}{100} =$ _____ %

Rename each decimal as a percent.

5. $0.42 =$ _____   6. $0.08 =$ _____   7. $1.5 =$ _____   8. $7.36 =$ _____

Rename each percent as a decimal.

9. $23\% =$ _____   10. $4\% =$ _____   11. $314\% =$ _____   12. $1,260\% =$ _____

13. Divide using a calculator to fill in the table. Study the first problem.

Fraction	Decimal	Percent	Percent (the nearest percent)
$\frac{1}{9}$	0./////////	//.//////// %	//%
$\frac{2}{3}$			
$\frac{3}{7}$			
$\frac{5}{9}$			
$\frac{7}{1}$			
$\frac{7}{8}$			

Use with Lesson 4.9.

Multiplying Fractions and Mixed Numbers

Solve.

1. $\frac{1}{4}$ of 16 _____

2. $\frac{6}{8}$ of 120 _____

3. 50% of 60 _____

4. $\frac{1}{4}$ of 2 _____

5. 25% of $\frac{2}{5}$ _____

6. $\frac{4}{6}$ of $\frac{4}{5}$ _____

Multiply. Write each answer in simplest form. If possible, write answers as mixed numbers or whole numbers.

7. $\frac{2}{5} * \frac{3}{8} =$ _____

8. $\frac{1}{3} * \frac{1}{2} =$ _____

9. $\frac{2}{3} * \frac{4}{5} =$ _____

10. $\frac{4}{9} * \frac{3}{8} =$ _____

11. $1\frac{2}{3} * 2\frac{1}{5} =$ _____

12. $3\frac{1}{4} * 2\frac{3}{4} =$ _____

13. $1\frac{2}{5} * 3 =$ _____

14. $2\frac{5}{6} * 2\frac{1}{2} =$ _____

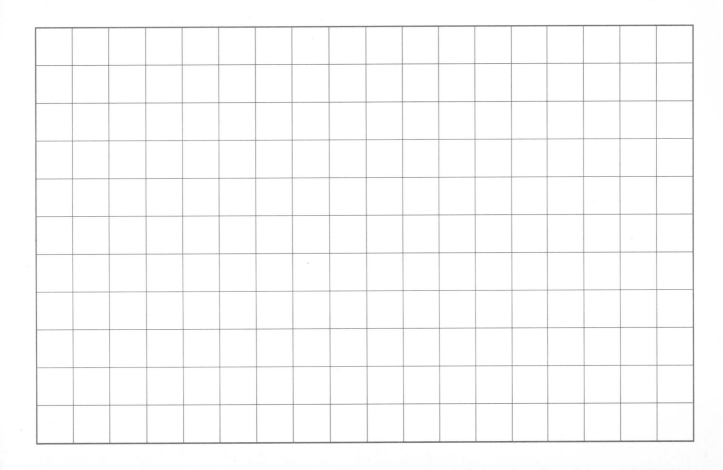

Math Boxes 4.9

---

1. Find the measure of ∠N without measuring the angle.

Measure of ∠N = _____°.

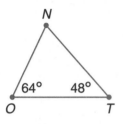

215

2. Write the following fractions in order from smallest to largest:

$$\frac{7}{8} \qquad \frac{1}{5} \qquad \frac{99}{100} \qquad \frac{6}{10} \qquad \frac{5}{12}$$

_____

70

---

3. Use division to rename the fraction as a decimal. Then rename the decimal as a percent.

$$\frac{7}{12} = 0.\text{_____} = \text{_____}\%$$

32–34

4. Fill in the missing numbers.

Fraction	Decimal	Percent
$\frac{3}{4}$		
	0.25	
		40%
$\frac{1}{3}$		
		65%
	0.9	

36 37

---

5. Complete.

a. $\frac{1}{8}$ of 48 = _____

b. $\frac{5}{9}$ of 90 = _____

c. $\frac{2}{7}$ of 35 = _____

d. $\frac{3}{4}$ of 64 = _____

e. $\frac{4}{5}$ of 800 = _____

83

6. Sonia bought $3\frac{5}{8}$ yards of fabric to make a dress. The pattern for the dress calls for only $2\frac{1}{3}$ yards of fabric. How much fabric will be left to make something else?

_____
(unit)

SRB
239

Use with Lesson 4.9.

How to Draw a Circle Graph

To draw a circle graph:

A. Express each part of the data as a percent of the total.

B. Use the Percent Circle on your Geometry Template to divide a circle and its interior (the total) into sectors whose sizes correspond to the percent form of the data.

1. Art, Barb, and Cyrus ran for sixth-grade class president. The election results are shown in the table below. Fill in the percent column. Then use your Percent Circle to draw a circle graph of the data.

Election Results		
Name	**Number of Votes**	**Percent of Total Vote**
Art	8	
Barb	10	
Cyrus	22	
Total	40	100%

Election Results

2. Doug, Bree, and Fred drove from Denver to Kansas City. The number of hours each one drove is shown in the table below. Fill in the percent column. Then use your Percent Circle to draw a circle graph of the data.

Driving Times		
Name	**Number of Hours**	**Percent of Total Time**
Doug	5	
Bree	4.5	
Fred	3	
Total	12.5	100%

Driving Times

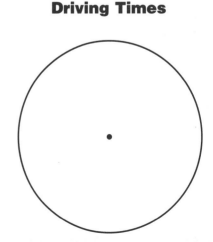

How Much Does Your Garbage Weigh?

Composition of Garbage Generated, per Person per Day

Material[1]	1960	1980	2000	2005[2]
	Weight (pounds)			
Paper and paperboard	0.91	1.32	1.77	1.88
Glass	0.20	0.36	0.24	0.22
Metals	0.32	0.35	0.36	0.37
Plastics	0.01	0.19	0.47	0.53
Other (rubber, textiles, wood)	0.24	0.44	0.68	0.75
Food wastes	0.37	0.32	0.46	0.46
Yard trimmings	0.61	0.66	0.46	0.46
Total garbage generated	2.66	3.64	4.44	4.67

Source: United States Environmental Protection Agency

[1]Included in table: household garbage and appliances; garbage from offices, businesses, restaurants, schools, hospitals, and libraries. Not included in table: car bodies, sludge, industrial and agricultural wastes.

[2]Projected

1. The percent column for 1960 has been completed in the table below. Complete the percent column for 2000. Round each answer to the nearest percent.

Material	1960		2000	
	Weight (pounds)	Percent of Total Weight	Weight (pounds)	Percent of Total Weight
Paper and paperboard	0.91	34%	1.77	
Glass	0.20	8%	0.24	
Metals	0.32	12%	0.36	
Plastics	0.01	0% (< 0.004%)	0.47	
Other (rubber, textiles, wood)	0.24	9%	0.68	
Food wastes	0.37	14%	0.46	
Yard trimmings	0.61	23%	0.46	
Total garbage generated	2.66	100%	4.44	

How Much Does Your Garbage Weigh? (cont.)

2. Study the circle graph for the 1960 data. Then draw a circle graph for the 2000 data. Remember to graph the smallest sector first.

Garbage by Weight—1960

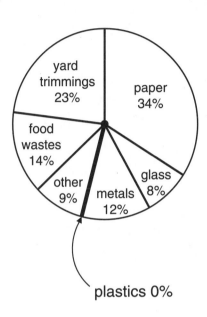

plastics 0%

Garbage by Weight—2000

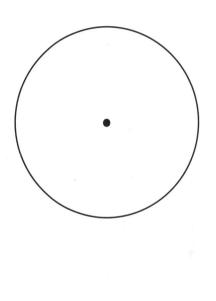

3. What material makes up the largest part of Americans' garbage, by weight? _____

4. According to projections for the year 2005, about how many pounds of garbage will a person generate, on average

   in a day? _____   in 1 week? _____   in 1 month (30 days)? _____

5. About how many months will it take a person to generate 1 ton of garbage in 2005? _____

6. Describe the changes that have taken place in the composition of garbage from 1960 to 2000.

   _____

   _____

   _____

   _____

Math Boxes 4.10

---

1. Measure the angle to the nearest degree.

Measure of reflex $\angle DEN$ is _____ °.

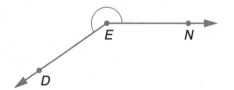

2. Compare. Write < or > .

a. $\dfrac{4}{5}$ _____ $\dfrac{5}{4}$

b. $\dfrac{7}{8}$ _____ $\dfrac{7}{15}$

c. $\dfrac{7}{12}$ _____ $\dfrac{8}{18}$

d. $\dfrac{1}{9}$ _____ $\dfrac{1}{5}$

---

3. Evaluate the following algebraic expressions for $s = 2\dfrac{1}{4}$.

a. $s + 1\dfrac{5}{8}$ _____

b. $9 - s$ _____

c. $s * 1\dfrac{1}{4}$ _____

d. $s - 1\dfrac{3}{8}$ _____

4. Multiply. Write each answer in simplest form.

a. $\dfrac{4}{5} * \dfrac{7}{8} =$ _____

b. $\dfrac{11}{12} * \dfrac{5}{10} =$ _____

c. $1\dfrac{3}{4} * 2\dfrac{1}{5} =$ _____

d. $2\dfrac{1}{3} * 3\dfrac{1}{2} =$ _____

e. $\dfrac{5}{9} * 1\dfrac{1}{6} =$ _____

---

5. This spreadsheet shows Evelyn's and Ann's scores on their first three spelling tests.

a. What is shown in Cell C2?

_____

	A	B	C	D	E
1	Student	Test 1	Test 2	Test 3	Average Score
2	Evelyn	95	90	85	
3	Ann	80	75	100	

b. Calculate the values for Cells E2 and E3 and enter them in the spreadsheet.

c. Circle the correct formula for Evelyn's average score on Tests 1 through 3.

(A2 + B2 + C3) / 3   (B1 + B2 + B3) / 3   (B2 + C2 + D2) / 3

Percent Problems

Math Message

A CD that regularly costs $15 is on sale for 20% off.

1. What is the discount in dollars?   _____

2. What is the sale price?   _____

Do *not* use a calculator to solve Problems 3–5.

3. A boom box that costs $120 is on sale for 25% off.

   a. What is the discount in dollars?   _____

   b. What is the sale price?   _____

4. A bank gives interest of 5% a year.

   a. What is the interest on $100.00?   _____

   b. What is the interest on $500.00?   _____

   c. What is the interest on $1,000.00?   _____

5. The $2.50 price of a hot dog at a major league baseball park is shared as follows:
   20% pays for the hot dog, bun, and fixings
   20% pays the concession stand workers
   10% is profit for the concession stand owner
   10% pays for cleaning and other costs
   40% goes to the team and stadium owners

   a. How much do the hot dog, bun, and fixings cost?   _____

   b. How much do the team and stadium owners get?   _____

   c. How much does the concession stand owner get?   _____

   Source: Zillions Magazine

You may use a calculator to solve the rest of the problems.

6. A CD that regularly costs $14.95 is on sale for 20% off.

   a. What is the discount in dollars? _____

   b. What is the sale price?   _____

Use with Lesson 4.11.

Percent Problems (cont.)

7. The table below shows the results of a science test given to 2,000 adults. Find the number of people who answered each question correctly.

Question	Percent Correct	Number of People
How long does it take Earth to go around the Sun? One day, one month, or one year? Answer: one year	48%	
Electrons are smaller than atoms. Answer: true	44%	
The universe began with a huge explosion. Answer: true	32%	
The earliest humans lived at the same time as the dinosaurs. Answer: false	51%	

Source: Science and Engineering Indicators—1998

8. In 1998, there were about 38 million elementary school students in the United States. The number of elementary school students is expected to increase by 3% between 1998 and 2006.

   a. About how many *more* elementary school students will there be in 2006? _____

   b. About how many elementary students will there be *in all* in 2006? _____

Source: National Center for Education Statistics

9. Elementary school students make up about 15% of the U.S. population. About how many elementary school students would you expect to live in a town with a population of 50,000? _____

Divide to Rename Fractions as Decimals and Percents

For each fraction, use the partial-quotients division algorithm to divide the
numerator by the denominator. Round the result to the nearest hundredth
and rename it as a percent.

1. $\frac{4}{7}$ = 0._____ = _____%   **2.** $\frac{7}{12}$ = 0._____ = _____%   **3.** $\frac{9}{16}$ = 0._____ = _____%

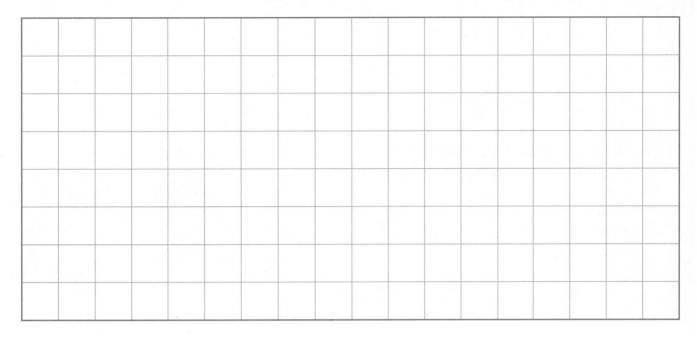

4. $\frac{5}{16}$ = 0._____ = _____%   **5.** $\frac{1}{15}$ = 0._____ = _____%   **6.** $\frac{11}{12}$ = _____ = _____%

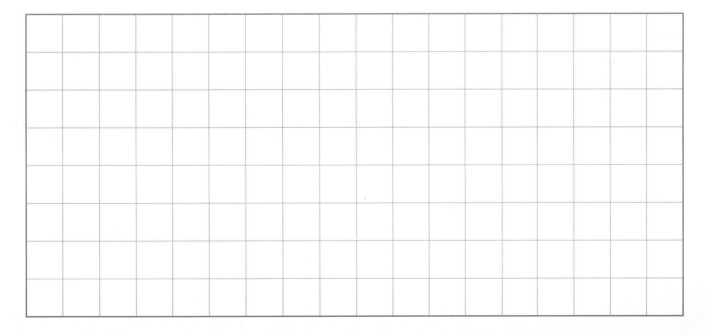

Math Boxes 4.11

---

1. Find the measure of ∠R without measuring the angle.

Measure of ∠R = _____°.

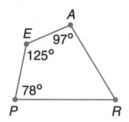

2. Write the following fractions in order from smallest to largest:

$$\frac{1}{20} \quad \frac{6}{7} \quad \frac{9}{10} \quad \frac{1}{3} \quad \frac{5}{8}$$

_____

---

3. Use division to rename the fraction as a decimal. Then rename the decimal as a percent.

$\frac{5}{6}$ = 0. _____ = _____%

4. Fill in the missing numbers.

Fraction	Decimal	Percent
$\frac{1}{5}$		
	0.625	
		60%
$\frac{2}{3}$		
		5%
	0.7	

---

5. Complete.

a. $\frac{2}{5}$ of 75 = _____

b. $\frac{3}{8}$ of 24 = _____

c. $\frac{5}{6}$ of 48 = _____

d. $\frac{1}{2}$ of $2\frac{1}{2}$ = _____

e. $\frac{3}{12}$ of 32 = _____

6. Martin is building two picture frames. He used $4\frac{1}{2}$ feet of lumber for one frame and $2\frac{3}{4}$ feet for the other frame. How many feet of lumber did he use in all?

_____

Time to Reflect

1. How good do you think you are at each of the skills listed below? Check the most appropriate box.

Skill	I'm very good.	I'm pretty good.	I need some practice.	I need a lot of practice.
a. Adding and subtracting fractions				
b. Adding and subtracting mixed numbers				
c. Multiplying fractions				
d. Multiplying mixed numbers				
e. Finding equivalent fractions, mixed numbers, decimals, and percents				

2. A sixth grade class was solving the problem $1\frac{3}{4} - \frac{2}{5}$.

Shawn solved it one way:

$$1\frac{3}{4} \quad 1\frac{15}{20}$$
$$-\;\frac{2}{5} \quad -\;\frac{8}{20}$$
$$\overline{\qquad\quad 1\frac{7}{20}}$$

Vanessa solved it a different way:

$$1\frac{3}{4} \qquad 1.75$$
$$-\;\frac{2}{5} \qquad -\;0.40$$
$$\overline{\qquad\qquad 1.35}$$

a. Did the two students get equivalent answers? _____

b. How could you confirm this? _____

_____

c. Do you prefer to do operations with fractions or decimals? _____

d. Does it matter? _____ Why or why not? _____

_____

1. The table below shows the results of a Bureau of the Census study of how people get to work. Use the Percent Circle to draw a circle graph of the results.

Method of Transportation	Percent of People
Drive alone	75.1%
Carpool	13.2%
Walk or work at home	5.3%
Take public transporation or other	6.4%

How People Get to Work

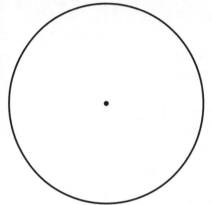

2. Draw and label the following angles.

   a. ∠LAG 72°

   b. ∠AND 125°

3. Measure each angle to the nearest degree.

   a.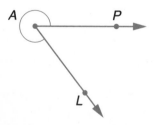

   b.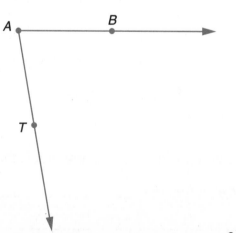

   Measure of reflex ∠LAP is _____°.

   Measure of ∠TAB is _____°.

Date _____   Time _____

Measuring and Drawing Angles with a Protractor

Math Message

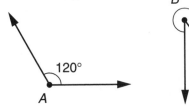

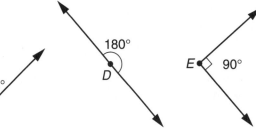

Which of the above angles is

1. a right angle? ∠ _____

2. an acute angle? ∠ _____

3. a reflex angle? ∠ _____

4. an obtuse angle? ∠ _____

5. a straight angle? ∠ _____

6. Use your full-circle protractor to measure each angle below. Measure carefully, but remember that measurements are never exact.

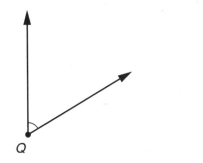

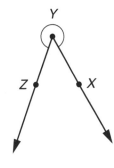

a. ∠Q measures about _____.

b. ∠XYZ measures about _____.

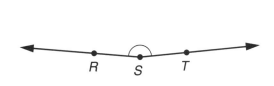

c. ∠RST measures about _____.

d. ∠W measures about _____.

Measuring and Drawing Angles with a Protractor (cont.)

7. Use your half-circle protractor to measure each angle below.

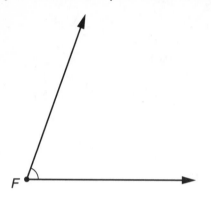

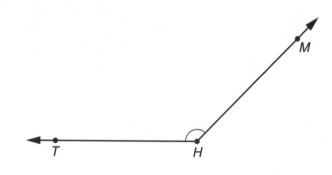

a. ∠F measures about _____.

b. ∠THM measures about _____.

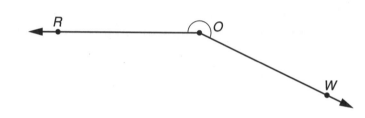

c. ∠P measures about _____.

d. ∠ROW measures about _____.

8. Draw and label the following angles. Use your half-circle protractor.

a. ∠DOR: 43°

b. ∠CAN: 165°

Date_____   Time_____

"Percent of" Problems

Solve mentally.

1. 10% of 20 = _____   **2.** 20% of 50 = _____

3. 25% of 320 = _____   **4.** 40% of 25 = _____

5. 50% of 36 = _____   **6.** 15% of 200 = _____

7. 75% of 120 = _____   **8.** 60% of 45 = _____

9. Choose one problem from Problems 1–8. Explain the strategy you used to solve that problem.

_____

_____

_____

_____

Solve. You may use your calculator.

10. $33\frac{1}{3}$% of 48 = _____   **11.** 45% of 72 = _____

12. 68% of 19 = _____   **13.** 8% of 30 = _____

14. Choose one problem from Problems 10–13. Explain the strategy you used to solve that problem.

_____

_____

_____

_____

Math Boxes 5.1

---

1. Insert parentheses to make each sentence true.

  a. 42 / 12 / 2 = 7

  b. 18 + 5 * 2 = 46

  c. 125 − 25 * 5 = 0

  d. 20 − 16 / 2 * 15 = 30

  e. 12 * 6 − 22 / 5 = 10

2. A group of 193 sixth graders are entered in a 3-on-3 basketball tournament. How many complete teams of 3 players can be formed?

_____

What would you do about any "leftover" students?

_____

_____

_____

---

3. a. Draw a line segment that is $3\frac{3}{8}$ inches long.

  b. By how many inches would you need to extend the segment to get a line segment that is 5 inches long?

  _____

---

4. Multiply.

  a.   32   **b.**   814   **c.**   15   **d.**   307   **e.**   625
         * 69   * 29   * 72   * 28   * 47

Use with Lesson 5.1.

Angle Relationships

Math Message

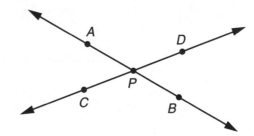

Measure angles *APC*, *DPB*, *APD*, and *CPB*. Write the measures below.

(*Note:* "m ∠*APC*" is short for "the measure of angle *APC*.")

1. m ∠*APC* = _____   m ∠*DPB* = _____

2. m ∠*APD* = _____   m ∠*CPB* = _____

3. What do you notice about the angle measures?

_____

_____

_____

Angles are sometimes named with small (lowercase) letters. Write the measures of the angles indicated in Problems 4–13. Do *not* use a protractor.

4.

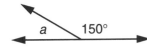

a   150°

m ∠*a* = _____

5.

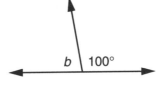

b   100°

m ∠*b* = _____

6.

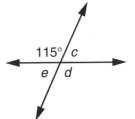

115° *c*
e / *d*

m ∠*c* = _____

m ∠*d* = _____

m ∠*e* = _____

7.

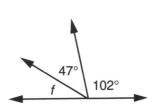

47°
f   102°

m ∠*f* = _____

Use with Lesson 5.2.

167

Angle Relationships (cont.)

8.

m ∠g = _____

9.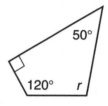

m ∠h = _____

m ∠i = _____

Reminder: The symbol ⌐ means that the angle is a right angle.

10.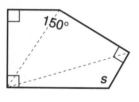

m ∠s = _____

11.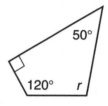

m ∠r = _____

12.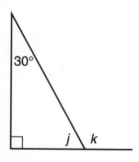

m ∠j = _____

m ∠k = _____

13.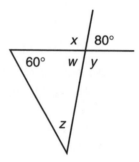

m ∠w = _____

m ∠x = _____

m ∠y = _____

m ∠z = _____

Math Boxes 5.2

1. Subtract. Do not use a calculator.

 a. $-2 - 5 =$ _____

 b. $4 - 7 =$ _____

 c. $8 - (-3) =$ _____

 d. $-6 - (-1) =$ _____

92 93

2. Rewrite each fraction pair with a common denominator.

 a. $\frac{3}{8}$ and $\frac{2}{3}$ _____

 b. $\frac{6}{9}$ and $\frac{4}{12}$ _____

 c. $\frac{2}{10}$ and $\frac{15}{25}$ _____

 d. $\frac{5}{11}$ and $\frac{6}{3}$ _____

73

3. Subtract. Show your work.

 a. 156.41
      $-$ 25.96

 b. 28.90
      $-$ 8.37

 c. 64.00
      $-$ 4.75

40 41

4. Complete the table.

Words	Exponential Notation	Base	Exponent	Calculator Key Sequence	Standard Notation
Nine to the third power				9 $\boxed{\wedge}$ 3 $\boxed{\text{Enter}}$	
Two to the twelfth power					
	5^{-6}	5	-6		

6

Using the Percent Circle

1. Jill, Jeremy, and Manuel were the candidates for homeroom student council representative. The table below shows the number of votes that each received. Find the fraction and percent of the votes that each received and record them in the table. Use your Percent Circle to draw a circle graph to display the results. Write a title for the graph.

Candidate	Number of Votes Received	Fraction of Votes Received	Percent of Votes Received
Jill	12		
Jeremy	7		
Manuel	6		

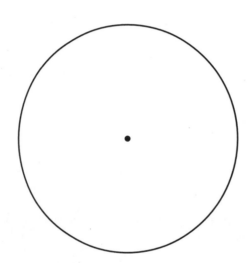

2. Look up the word *sector* in the *Student Reference Book* Glossary. Use your compass to draw a circle in the space at the right. Then use your protractor to divide the circle into 3 sectors by drawing a 155° sector and a 75° sector.

   What is the degree measure of the third sector? _____

Use with Lesson 5.3.

Drawing Circle Graphs with a Protractor

Mr. Li surveyed the students in his class to find out what kinds of pets they owned and how many of each kind they had. The results are shown in the first two columns of the table below.

Kind of Pet	Number of Pets	Fraction of Total Number of Pets	Decimal Equivalent (to nearest thousandth)	Percent of Total Number of Pets	Degree Measure of Sector
Dog	8	$\frac{8}{24}$	0.333	$33\frac{1}{3}\%$	$\frac{1}{3}$ * 360° = 120°
Cat	6				____ * 360° = ____
Guinea pig or hamster	3				____ * 360° = ____
Bird	3				____ * 360° = ____
Other	4				____ * 360° = ____

1. Complete the table above. Study the first row.

2. At the right, or on a separate sheet of paper, use a protractor to make a circle graph of the information in the table. If you need to, tape your completed circle graph on this page. Write a title for the graph.

Drawing Circle Graphs with a Protractor (cont.)

3. Sixth grade students at Hawthorn School took a survey about after-school activities. Students answering the survey named the activity on which they spent the most time after school. The results are shown in the table below. Complete the table.

Activity	Number of Students	Fraction of Students	Decimal Equivalent	Percent of Students (to nearest percent)	Size of Sector
Music	12				
Math Club	28				
Art	5				
Sports	8				
Computers	3				
None	4				

4. Make a circle graph on a separate sheet of paper to display the information in the table. Tape your completed circle graph in the space below. Write a title for the graph.

Use with Lesson 5.3.

Math Boxes 5.3

1. Solve each open sentence.

   a. $32 + n = 56$ Solution _____

   b. $y - 13 = 20$ Solution _____

   c. $48 = 4 * d$ Solution _____

   d. $(2 * m) + 5 = 17$ Solution _____

SRB 223–225

2. Tell whether the following numbers are prime or composite:

   a. The number of ounces in 1 cup

    _____

   b. The number of teaspoons in

    1 tablespoon _____

   c. The number of square
    feet in 1 square yard

    _____

SRB 12

3. The circumference of a light pole is about 25 inches.

   a. What is its diameter?

    About _____ in.

   b. What is its radius?

    About _____ in.

SRB 195

4. Multiply mentally.

   a. $30 * 1.5 =$ _____

   b. $7.3 * 20 =$ _____

   c. _____ $= 0.37 * 100$

   d. _____ $= 1.68 * 10$

   e. _____ $= 50 * 0.6$

SRB 43 44

5. Complete.

   a. $\frac{1}{3}$ of $27 =$ _____

   b. _____ $= \frac{5}{6}$ of 30

   c. _____ $= \frac{4}{7}$ of 42

   d. _____ $= \frac{2}{5}$ of 60

   e. $\frac{3}{8}$ of $56 =$ _____

SRB 83

6. Complete.

   a. _____ m $= 368$ mm

   b. _____ cm $= 0.245$ m

   c. 32 mm $=$ _____ m

   d. 45.2 cm $=$ _____ mm

   e. 0.25 mm $=$ _____ cm

SRB 192

The Coordinate Grid

1. Plot and label the following points on the coordinate grid below. The first one has been done for you.

   A: (3,1)   B: (2,5)   C: $\left(-4,-\frac{1}{2}\right)$ D: (−6,−9)   E: (0,3)   F: (−2.5,0)

2. Write the ordered number pair for each of the following points shown on the coordinate grid below.

   G: (_____,_____)   H: (_____,_____)   I: (_____,_____)

   J: (_____,_____)   K: (_____,_____)   L: (_____,_____)

   M: (_____,_____)   N: (_____,_____)

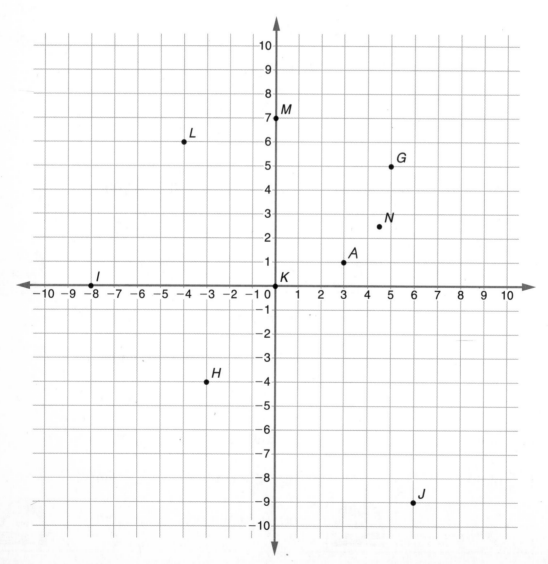

Use with Lesson 5.4.

Polygons on a Coordinate Grid

The names of polygons consist of letters that name the vertices, written in consecutive order. For example, the square at the right may be named square *ABCD*, or *BCDA*, or *CDAB*, or *DABC*. Squares *ACBD* and *ADBC* are examples of incorrect names.

The points shown on the grid below represent vertices of polygons. One or two vertices are missing for each polygon. Plot and name the missing vertices on the grid and then draw each polygon. List the number pairs for the missing vertices.

1. Scalene triangle *ABC*

   C: (_____,_____)

2. Right triangle *DEF*, which is also an isosceles triangle

   F: (_____,_____)

3. Square *GHIJ*

   I: (_____,_____)

   J: (_____,_____)

4. Rectangle *KLMN*, with $\overline{LM} = 2 * \overline{KL}$

   M: (_____,_____)

   N: (_____,_____)

5. Isosceles triangle *OPQ*, with $\overline{OP}$ the longest side

   Q: (_____,_____)

6. Parallelogram *RSTU*

   U: (_____,_____)

7. Rhombus *VWXY*

   W: (_____,_____)

   Y: (_____,_____)

8. Kite *A'D'P'R'*

   P': (_____,_____)   *R'*: (_____,_____)

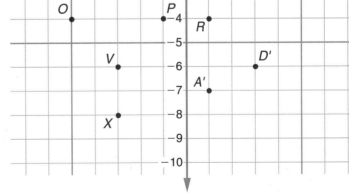

Midpoint of a Line Segment

The **midpoint** of a line segment is the point halfway between the endpoints of the segment.

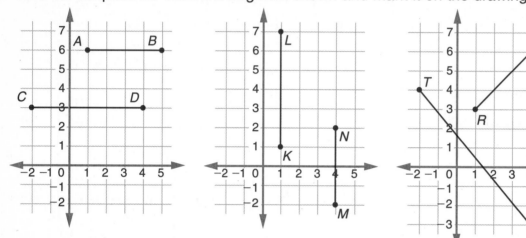

C is the midpoint of $\overline{AB}$. E is the midpoint of $\overline{MN}$. W is the midpoint of $\overline{RS}$.

1. Find the midpoint for each line segment shown and mark it on the drawing.

2. Find the endpoints and midpoint for each of the following line segments from Problem 1 above. Study the first one, which has been done for you.

		Endpoints		Midpoint

a. $\overline{AB}$ (__1__ , __6__) (__5__ , __6__)   (__3__ , __6__)

b. $\overline{CD}$ (_____ , _____) (_____ , _____)   (_____ , _____)

c. $\overline{KL}$ (_____ , _____) (_____ , _____)   (_____ , _____)

d. $\overline{MN}$ (_____ , _____) (_____ , _____)   (_____ , _____)

e. $\overline{RS}$ (_____ , _____) (_____ , _____)   (_____ , _____)

f. $\overline{TU}$ (_____ , _____) (_____ , _____)   (_____ , _____)

3. Look for a pattern in your answers to Problem 2. If you know the coordinates of the endpoints of a line segment, how can you find the coordinates of the midpoint of the segment without plotting the line segment on a coordinate grid?

_____

_____

Making a Circle Graph with a Protractor

1. One way to convert a percent to the degree measure of a sector is to multiply 360° by the decimal equivalent of the percent.

    Example What is the degree measure of a sector that is 55% of a circle?
    55% of 360° = 0.55 * 360° = 198°

55%

Complete the table below.

Percent of Circle	Decimal Equivalent	Degree Measure of Sector
40%		0.4 * 360° = _____
90%		
65%		
5%		
1%		

2. The table below shows the elective courses taken by a class of seventh graders. Complete the table. Then, in the space to the right, use a protractor to make a circle graph to display the information. Do not use the Percent Circle. (*Reminder:* Use either a fraction or decimal to find the degree measure of each sector.) Write a title for the graph.

Course	Number of Students	Fraction of Students	Decimal Equivalent	Percent of Students	Degree Measure of Sector
Music	6				
Art	9				
Computers	10				
Photography	5				

Math Boxes 5.4

---

1. Insert parentheses to make each sentence true.

   a. 18 + 2 / 5 + 5 = 9

   b. 72 / 8 + 4 / 6 = 1

   c. 72 / 8 + 4 / 6 = $9\frac{2}{3}$

   d. 95 − 10 / 3 + 2 = 93

   e. 74 * $\frac{1}{2}$ + $\frac{1}{2}$ + 1 = 148

2. Frank saved $93 for his birthday celebration. He wants to take some friends to a baseball game. If tickets cost $8 apiece, how many tickets can he buy?

_____

---

3. a. Draw a line segment that is 8.6 centimeters long.

b. By how many centimeters would you need to extend the segment to get a line segment that is 10 centimeters long?

_____

---

4. Multiply.

   a.   56
       * 23

   b.   708
       * 83

   c.   16
       * 59

   d.   124
       * 38

   e.   263
       * 97

Use with Lesson 5.4.

Translations, Reflections, and Rotations

Plot and label the vertices of the image that would result from each translation.
One vertex of each image has already been plotted and labeled.

1.

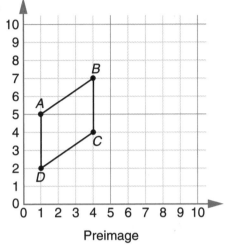

Preimage

horizontal
translation

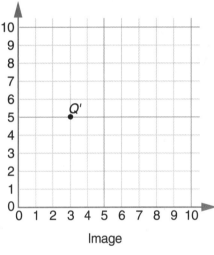

Image

2.

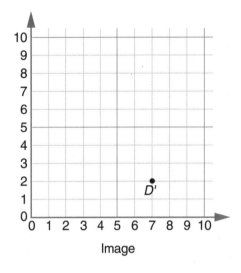

Preimage

vertical
translation

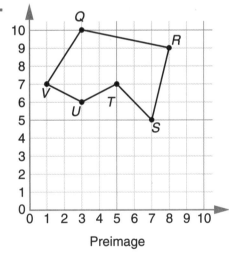

Image

3.

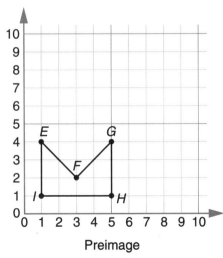

Preimage

diagonal
translation

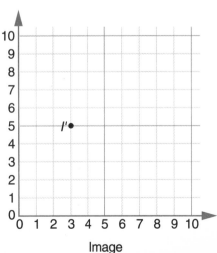

Image

Translations, Reflections, and Rotations (cont.)

Use your Geometry Template to draw the reflected image of each geometric design below. Line *AB* is the line of reflection.

4.

5.

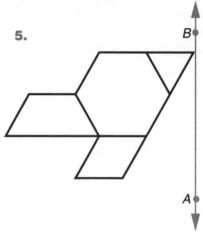

Write the number of degrees of rotation needed to produce each given image. The point of rotation is marked. You might find it helpful to copy the figures onto a piece of paper using your Geometry Template. Then rotate the paper to find the given number of degrees.

6.

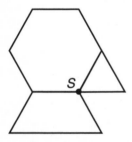

Preimage

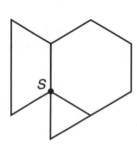

Image

_____ counterclockwise

7.

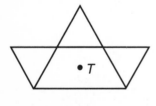

Preimage

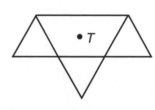

Image

_____ clockwise

Use with Lesson 5.5.

Translations, Reflections, and Rotations (cont.)

As in Problems 6 and 7, you might find it helpful to copy the figures onto a piece of paper.

Use your Geometry Template to draw the result of each rotation.
The point of rotation is marked.

8.

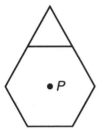

90° clockwise   180° clockwise   270° clockwise

9.

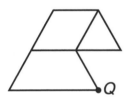

90° clockwise   180° clockwise   270° clockwise

10.

90° clockwise   180° clockwise   270° clockwise

Drawing and Measuring Angles

Use your protractor to measure the angles below.

1.

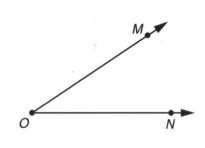

∠*MON* is about _____.

2.

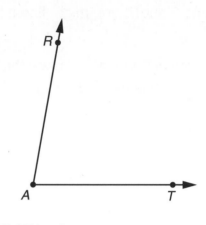

∠*RAT* is about _____.

3.

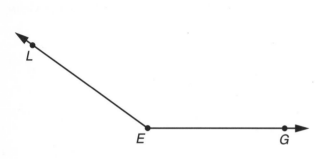

∠*LEG* is about _____.

4.

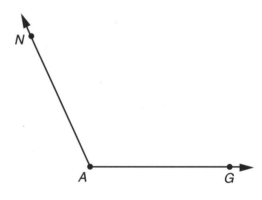

∠*NAG* is about _____.

Find the angle measures in each of the regular polygons below. Write the measure for each angle inside the polygon.

5.

6.

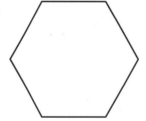

7.

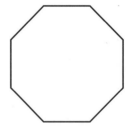

8. Draw and label a reflex angle.

9. Draw and label a straight angle.

∠ _____ is about _____.

∠ _____ is about _____.

Math Boxes 5.5

1. Subtract. Do not use a calculator.

   a. $-5 - 9 = $ _____

   b. $-6 - 8 = $ _____

   c. $-12 - (-3) = $ _____

   d. $5 - (-2) = $ _____

2. Rewrite each fraction pair with a common denominator.

   a. $\frac{6}{8}$ and $\frac{8}{25}$ _____

   b. $\frac{7}{10}$ and $\frac{19}{20}$ _____

   c. $\frac{4}{5}$ and $\frac{3}{9}$ _____

   d. $\frac{6}{7}$ and $\frac{2}{5}$ _____

3. Subtract. Show your work.

   a.
   $$\begin{array}{r} 23.72 \\ -\ 15.09 \\ \hline \end{array}$$

   b.
   $$\begin{array}{r} 7.30 \\ -\ 2.81 \\ \hline \end{array}$$

   c.
   $$\begin{array}{r} 25.00 \\ -\ 0.25 \\ \hline \end{array}$$

4. Complete the table.

Words	Exponential Notation	Base	Exponent	Repeated Factors	Standard Notation
		10	8		
				8 * 8 * 8 * 8 * 8	
				0.1 * 0.1 * 0.1	

Congruent Figures

Math Message

Carefully examine the figures in Examples a–f.

The following pairs of figures
are **congruent** to each other.

The following pairs of figures are
not congruent to each other.

a.

d.

b.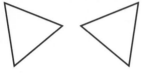

e.

c.

f.

1. Write a definition of "congruent polygons." Then compare your definition to the definition on page 166 in your *Student Reference Book*.

_____

Line segments are **congruent** if they have the same length.	Angles are **congruent** if they have the same degree measure.

2. Draw wavy lines to connect each pair of congruent line segments below. Use a ruler to measure line segments if needed to help you.

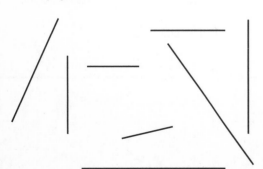

3. Draw wavy lines to connect each pair of congruent angles below. Use a protractor to measure angles if needed to help you.

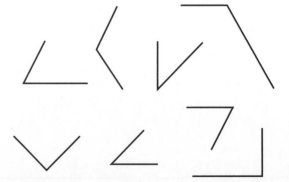

Use with Lesson 5.6.

Constructing Congruent Figures

You may use any of your construction tools—ruler, compass, protractor, or Geometry Template—to complete the constructions below. Tracing is not allowed.

1. Draw a triangle that is congruent to triangle *RST*.

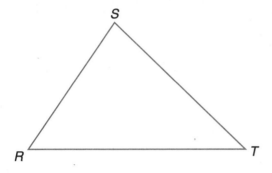

2. Draw a line segment *BC* so that $\overline{BC}$ is congruent to $\overline{AB}$ and the measure of angle *ABC* is 45°.

3. The plan below is for a paper cone with a glue tab. All dimensions and angle measures are shown. Make a congruent copy of the plan. Draw your copy on a separate sheet of paper. Cut out your copy and tape it on top of the plan below.

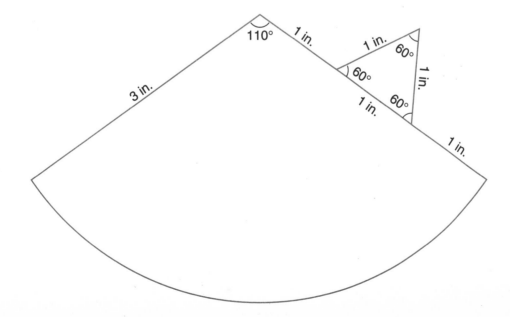

Rough Sketches and Accurate Drawings

Roberta wants to build a bird feeder. She has found a plan for a feeder in a library book.

Here is Roberta's rough sketch for one side of the feeder. The lengths and angle measures are correct, but the drawing is not accurate.

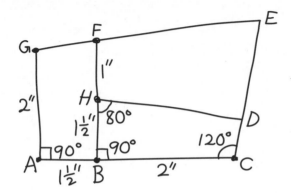

Make an accurate drawing of Roberta's rough sketch. Mark and label points A, B, C, D, E, F, G, and H on your drawing.

Math Boxes 5.6

---

1. Solve each open sentence.

    a. $12 / x = 2$ Solution _____

    b. $d / 12 = 2$ Solution _____

    c. $3 - (3 * b) = 0$ Solution _____

    d. $5 * (8 - n) = 15$ Solution _____

2. Circle the prime numbers.

    7   15   23   39   68   92

---

3. Draw a circle whose diameter is 5 cm. Calculate the radius and circumference to the nearest 0.1 cm.

    $r =$ _____ cm $C =$ _____ cm

4. Multiply mentally.

    a. $5 * 8,050 =$ _____

    b. $50 * 63 =$ _____

    c. _____ $= 500 * 120$

    d. _____ $= 500 * 146$

    e. _____ $= 25 * 35 * 4$

---

5. Complete.

    a. $\frac{2}{3}$ of 21 = _____

    b. _____ $= \frac{3}{4}$ of 80

    c. _____ $= \frac{2}{9}$ of 27

    d. _____ $= \frac{4}{5}$ of 40

    e. $\frac{1}{2}$ of 25 = _____

6. Complete.

    a. 15 m = _____ cm

    b. 25 cm = _____ m

    c. 143 mm = _____ cm

    d. 2.06 cm = _____ mm

    e. _____ mm = 1.43 m

Constructing Line Segments

Use only a compass, straightedge, and sharp pencil for the constructions below.
Use rulers and protractors only to check your work. Tracing is not allowed.

1. Copy this line segment. Label the endpoints of your copy A' and B'. (These symbols
   are read "A prime" and "B prime.")

   A   B

2. Construct a line segment twice as long as $\overline{CD}$. Label the endpoints of your segment
   C' and D'.

   C   D

3. Construct a line segment as long as $\overline{EF}$ and $\overline{GH}$ together. Label the endpoints of
   your segment E' and H'.

   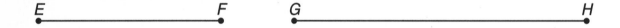
   E   F   G   H

Challenge

4. Construct a segment with a length equal to the length of $\overline{IJ}$ minus the length of $\overline{KL}$.
   Label the endpoints of your segment I' and K'.

   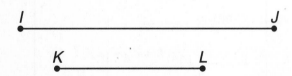
   I   J
   K   L

                                          Use with Lesson 5.7.

Constructing Triangles

Use only a compass, straightedge, and sharp pencil for the constructions below.
Use rulers and protractors to check your work. Tracing is not allowed.

Do your constructions on another piece of paper. If your compass has a sharp point,
work on top of a piece of cardboard or a stack of several sheets of paper. When you
are satisfied with a construction, cut it out and tape it onto this page.

1. Copy triangle *ABC*. Label the vertices of your copy *A'*, *B'*, and *C'*.

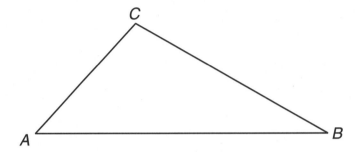

2. Construct a triangle with each side
   the same length as $\overline{DE}$.

3. Use a ruler to draw a line segment
   2 inches long and another line segment
   3 inches long. Then use a compass
   and straightedge to construct a triangle
   with sides 2 inches, 2 inches, and
   3 inches long.

Challenge

4. Is it possible to draw a triangle with sides 3 inches, 3 inches, and 7 inches long? _____

   Explain. _____

   _____

Circle Graphs

Convert the following percents to degree measures on a circle graph.

1. 27% _____

2. 49% _____

3. 73% _____

4. 98% _____

5. 65% _____

Convert the following fractions to degree measures on a circle graph.

6. $\frac{3}{8}$ _____

7. $\frac{6}{9}$ _____

8. $\frac{4}{5}$ _____

9. $\frac{8}{12}$ _____

10. $\frac{3}{4}$ _____

11. Use your protractor to divide the circle into three sectors by drawing a 48° sector and a 116° sector.

What is the degree measure of the third sector?

_____

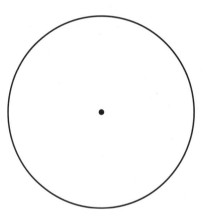

12. Ms. Camponella's sixth graders were having a surprise birthday party for her. The table shows how many students signed up to bring each kind of treat.

a. Complete the table.

Treat	Number Signed Up	Degree Measure of Sector
Chips	8	
Cookies	5	
Drinks	3	
Fruit	9	

b. Use your protractor to make a circle graph that displays the information.

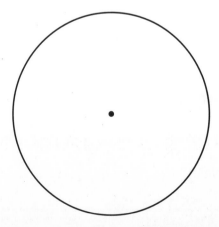

Use with Lesson 5.7.

Math Boxes 5.7

1. Multiply. Write your answer in simplest form.

   a. $\frac{3}{8} * \frac{3}{4} =$ _____

   b. $\frac{2}{9} * \frac{5}{7} =$ _____

   c. _____ $= \frac{6}{9} * \frac{3}{8}$

   d. _____ $= \frac{5}{4} * \frac{9}{8}$

   e. $\frac{6}{10} * \frac{5}{6} =$ _____

   SRB
   84 85

2. Two of the lines shown are parallel. Without using a protractor, find the degree measure of each numbered angle. Write each measure on the drawing.

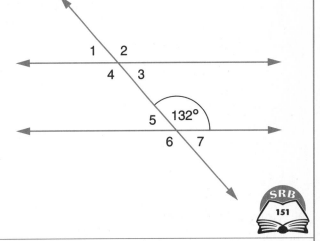

   SRB
   151

3. Which set of data displayed below has the following landmarks: maximum 27, mode 21, median 19, and minimum 8? Circle the letter of the best choice.

   a.

Stems (10s)	Leaves (1s)
0	8 9
1	1 3 3 7 9
2	1 1 1 2 6 7

   b.

8	/ /
9	/ / /
12	/ /
15	/ /
19	/
21	/
24	/ / /
27	/

   c.

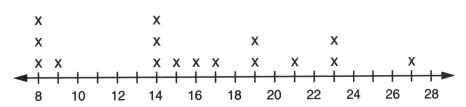

   SRB
   128–130

Compass-and-Straightedge Constructions

Use with Lesson 5.8.

Use only a compass, straightedge, and sharp pencil. Use rulers and protractors only to check your work. Tracing is not allowed. Do your constructions on another piece of paper. When you are satisfied with a construction, cut it out and tape it onto this page.

1. Copy this angle. When you are finished, check your work with a protractor.

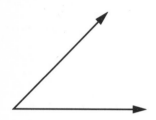

2. Copy this quadrangle.

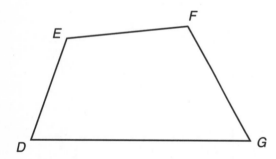

3. Construct a triangle that is the same shape as triangle *ABC* below but that has sides twice as long.

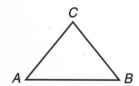

Compass-and-Straightedge Constructions (cont.)

Use only a compass, straightedge, and sharp pencil. Use rulers and protractors only to check your work. Tracing is not allowed.

4. Construct a perpendicular bisector of this line segment.

_____

5. Divide this line segment into four equal parts.

_____

6. To **inscribe** a square in a circle means to construct a square inside a circle so that all four vertices (corners) of the square are on the circle. Draw a circle. Then inscribe a square in it.

7. Use your Geometry Template to draw a parallelogram. Then construct a line segment to show the height of the parallelogram. (That is, construct a perpendicular segment from one side to the opposite side.)

Math Boxes 5.8

1. Write a number sentence for each word sentence. Then tell whether the number sentence is true or false.

Word Sentence	Number Sentence	True or False?
Five times eight is equal to 45.		
15 is greater than 2 less than 10.		
If 72 is divided by the square of 3, the result is 8.		

SRB 223–225

2. Rename each fraction as a mixed number.

a. $\frac{8}{5}$ = _____

b. $\frac{33}{9}$ = _____

c. $\frac{42}{8}$ = _____

d. $\frac{37}{3}$ = _____

e. $\frac{46}{9}$ = _____

SRB 67

3. Complete.

a. 8 million = _____ thousands

b. 25 billion = _____ millions

c. 23.5 million = _____ millions, _____ thousands

d. 0.7 billion = _____ millions

SRB 4

4. Divide.

a. $\frac{523}{18}$ → _____

b. $\frac{2,609}{73}$ → _____

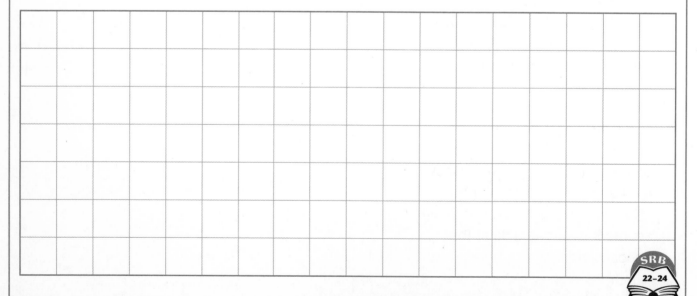
SRB 22–24

Use with Lesson 5.8.

Angle Measures

Write the measures of the angles indicated in Problems 1–6.
Do *not* use a protractor.

1. m $\angle a$ = _____

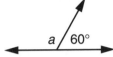

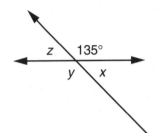

2. m $\angle x$ = _____   m $\angle y$ = _____   m $\angle z$ = _____

3. m $\angle p$ = _____

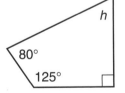

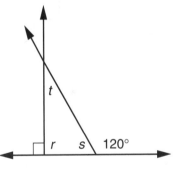

4. m $\angle r$ = _____   m $\angle s$ = _____   m $\angle t$ = _____

5. m $\angle h$ = _____

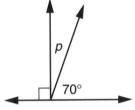

6. m $\angle d$ = _____   m $\angle e$ = _____

    m $\angle f$ = _____   m $\angle g$ = _____

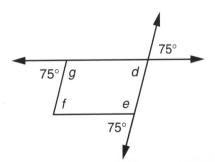

Parallel Lines and Angle Relationships

Without measuring with a protractor, find the degree measure of each angle in Problems 1–6 below. Write the measure inside the angle. Then circle the figures in which two of the lines appear to be parallel.

1.

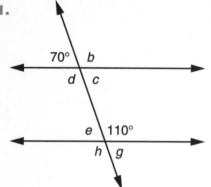

2.

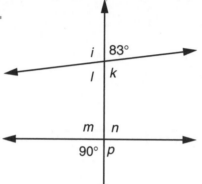

3.

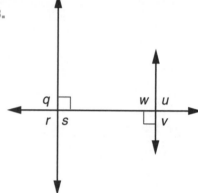

4.

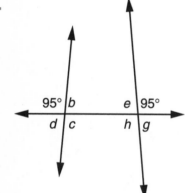

5.

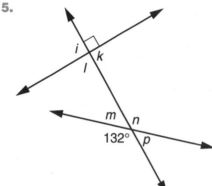

6.

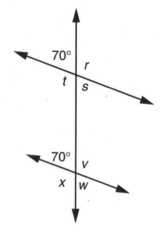

7. A line that intersects two parallel lines is called a **transversal.** The angles formed by two parallel lines and a transversal have special properties. Refer to the picture of parallel lines below to describe these properties.

Example Angles *b* and *f* have the same measure.

_____

_____

_____

_____

_____

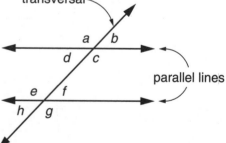

Working with Parallel Lines

1. Using only a compass and straightedge, construct two parallel lines. Do this construction without referring to the *Student Reference Book*. (*Hint:* This construction involves copying an angle.)

2. Draw two parallel lines using only a ruler and a pencil.

3. Draw a parallelogram that is not a rectangle using only a ruler and a pencil.

Operations with Fractions and Mixed Numbers

Add, subtract, or multiply. Write each answer in simplest form.

1. $2\frac{3}{6} + 3\frac{1}{2} =$ _____

2. $4\frac{7}{12} - 2\frac{3}{12} =$ _____

3. $4 - 2\frac{3}{5} =$ _____

4. $3\frac{1}{4} - 1\frac{3}{4} =$ _____

5. $5\frac{3}{5} - 2\frac{3}{10} =$ _____

6. $2\frac{1}{4} - 1\frac{2}{3} =$ _____

7. $\frac{3}{5} * 10 =$ _____

8. $\frac{2}{3} * \frac{4}{5} =$ _____

9. $3\frac{1}{2} * 2\frac{5}{6} =$ _____

Use with Lesson 5.9.

Math Boxes 5.9

1. Multiply. Write your answer in simplest form.

    a. $\frac{6}{7} * \frac{8}{10} =$ _____

    b. $\frac{9}{12} * \frac{3}{4} =$ _____

    c. _____ $= \frac{5}{2} * \frac{5}{6}$

    d. _____ $= \frac{3}{10} * \frac{5}{9}$

    e. $\frac{4}{6} * \frac{3}{8} =$ _____

2. Two of the lines shown are parallel. Without using a protractor, find the degree measure of each numbered angle. Write each measure on the drawing.

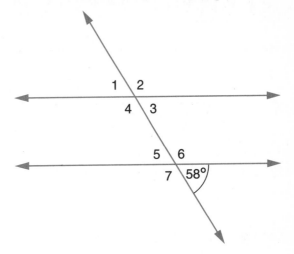

3. Which set of data displayed below has the following landmarks: maximum 40, mode 35, median 20, and minimum 0? Circle the letter of the best choice.

a.

Stems (10s)	Leaves (1s)
0	0 2 4 6
1	7 7 8 9
2	0
3	1 5 5 5 5 8
4	0 0 0

b.

0	/
3	/ /
15	/ /
20	/ / /
35	/ /
37	/ /
40	/

c.

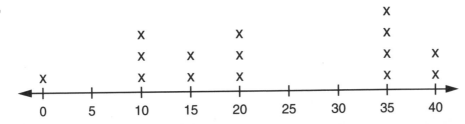

Properties of Parallelograms

1. The two lines below are parallel. Lay a ruler so that it intersects the parallel lines. Draw two transversals by drawing a line along each of the longer sides of the ruler. These lines should be parallel. The four lines form a parallelogram. Label the parallelogram *ABCD*.

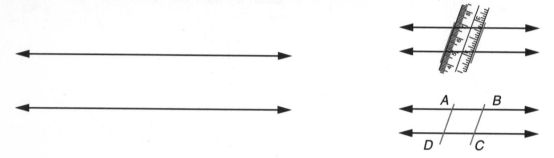

2. Use a compass to make sure that both pairs of opposite sides of your parallelogram are congruent.

3. Measure ∠*BAD* with a protractor. Write the measure on your drawing.

4. Find the measures of the other three angles of the parallelogram without measuring them with a protractor. Write the measures on your drawing.

5. Check your answers by measuring the angles with a protractor.

6. a. Angles *R* and *S* in the parallelogram at the right are opposite each other. Name another pair of opposite angles in the parallelogram.

   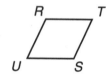

   _____

   b. What do you think is true about the opposite angles in a parallelogram?

   _____

7. a. Two angles of a polygon that are "next to each other" are called **consecutive angles.** Consecutive angles have a common side. Angles *R* and *U* in parallelogram *RUST* are consecutive angles. Name three other pairs of consecutive angles in this parallelogram.

   _____

   b. What do you think is true about consecutive angles in a parallelogram?

   _____

   _____

Parallelogram Problems

All figures on this page are parallelograms. Do not use a ruler or protractor to solve the problems below.

1. a. Measure of ∠A = _____. Explain.

_____

_____

_____

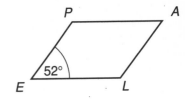

b. Measure of ∠L = _____. Explain.

_____

_____

_____

2. Length of $\overline{AB}$ = _____. Explain.

_____

_____

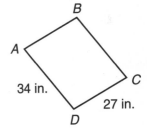

3. Measure of ∠OPT = _____. Explain.

_____

_____

_____

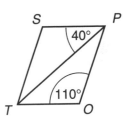

4. Quadrilateral *REST* is a square.

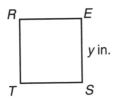

a. Measure of ∠R = _____

b. Length of $\overline{ES}$ = _____

c. Perimeter of
  square *REST* = _____

5. What is the perimeter of parallelogram *BOYS*?
  Hint: First find the value of *x*.

_____

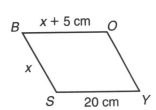

Parallelogram Problems (cont.)

6. Construct a parallelogram using only a compass and straightedge. Do this construction without referring to the *Student Reference Book*.

Challenge

7. Quadrilaterals *FAIR* and *FARE* are parallelograms. Without using a protractor, find the measure of the angles in parallelogram *FAIR*.

What is the measure of

∠*IAF*? _____   ∠*AIR*? _____

∠*IRF*? _____   ∠*RFA*? _____

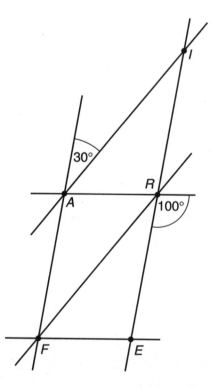

Use with Lesson 5.10.

Angle Problems

1. Line *AB* is a straight line. Angles *x* and *y* are congruent.

   What is the measure of ∠*x*? _____

   Explain how you got your answer.

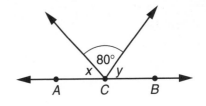

_____

_____

_____

2. Lines *WX* and *YZ* are parallel.

   What is the measure of ∠*a*? _____

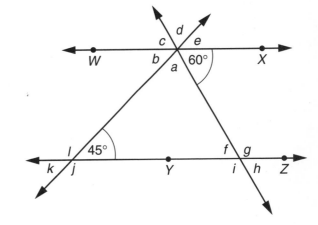

   Explain how you got your answer.

_____

_____

_____

3. Line segments *AB* and *CD* are parallel.

   What is the measure of ∠*w*? _____

   Explain how you got your answer.

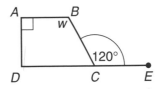

_____

_____

_____

Math Boxes 5.10

1. Write a number sentence for each word sentence. Then tell whether the number sentence is true or false.

Word Sentence	Number Sentence	True or False?
If 19 is subtracted from 55, the result is 36.		
78 added to 62 is less than 160.		
45 is 5 times as much as 9.		

2. Rename each mixed number as a fraction.

a. $12\frac{1}{8}$ = _____

b. $1\frac{7}{10}$ = _____

c. $2\frac{3}{4}$ = _____

d. $2\frac{6}{11}$ = _____

e. $5\frac{1}{3}$ = _____

3. Complete.

a. 6 million = _____ thousands

b. 37 billion = _____ millions

c. 1.6 billion = _____ millions

d. 9 billion = _____ thousands

4. Divide.

a. $6\overline{)792}$ → _____

b. $36\overline{)4,537}$ → _____

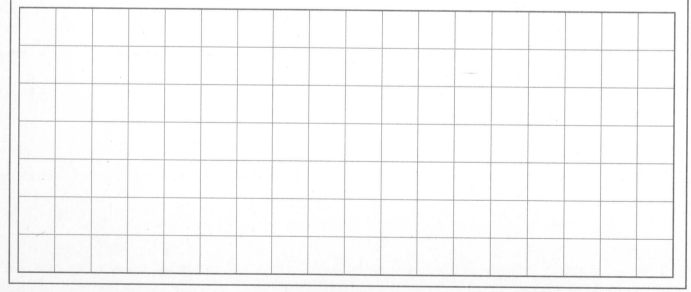

Use with Lesson 5.10.

Time to Reflect

1. In this unit, you had the opportunity to learn a second way to construct circle graphs. Which geometric tool do you find easier to use, the percent circle or the protractor? Explain why.

_____

_____

_____

_____

2. Which activity in this unit do you believe is an example of your best work? Why do you think so?

_____

_____

_____

_____

3. Which activity in this unit did you find the most challenging? Explain why.

_____

_____

_____

_____

4. What is something new you learned about geometry in this unit?

_____

_____

_____

_____

Math Boxes 5.11

---

1. Solve.

   a. $18 + n = 37$ Solution _____

   b. $5 * (x - 2) = 10$ Solution _____

   c. $6 = (\frac{b}{3}) + 6$ Solution _____

   d. $b - 4.5 = 5.5$ Solution _____

2. Subtract.

   a. _____ $= -5 - (-7)$

   b. _____ $= -3 - 8$

   c. _____ $= 12 - (-5)$

   d. _____ $= -6 - (-2)$

---

3. Make each sentence true by inserting parentheses.

   a. $5 + 5 - 3 * \frac{6}{6} = 7$

   b. $3 * 9 - 5 + \frac{8}{2} = 26$

   c. $36 / 6 + 3 - 3^2 = 0$

   d. $1\frac{3}{4} - \frac{1}{2} + \frac{5}{8} = 1\frac{7}{8}$

   e. $1\frac{3}{4} - \frac{1}{2} + \frac{5}{8} = \frac{5}{8}$

4. Multiply. Write your answer in simplest form.

   a. _____ $= \frac{3}{5} * \frac{2}{8}$

   b. _____ $= \frac{4}{9} * \frac{3}{6}$

   c. _____ $= \frac{5}{7} * \frac{3}{10}$

   d. $\frac{9}{11} * \frac{5}{6} =$ _____

   e. $\frac{2}{4} * \frac{3}{16} =$ _____

---

5. Write a word sentence for each number sentence.

   a. $48 / 12 - 6 = -2$

   _____

   _____

   _____

   _____

   b. $4^2 + 6 * 7 = 58$

   _____

   _____

   _____

   _____

                    Use with Lesson 5.11.

Reference

Metric System

Units of Length
1 kilometer (km)	= 1000 meters (m)
1 meter	= 10 decimeters (dm)
	= 100 centimeters (cm)
	= 1000 millimeters (mm)
1 decimeter	= 10 centimeters
1 centimeter	= 10 millimeters

Units of Area
1 square meter (m^2)	= 100 square decimeters (dm^2)
	= 10,000 square centimeters (cm^2)
1 square decimeter	= 100 square centimeters
1 are (a)	= 100 square meters
1 hectare (ha)	= 100 ares
1 square kilometer (km^2)	= 100 hectares

Units of Volume
1 cubic meter (m^3)	= 1000 cubic decimeters (dm^3)
	= 1,000,000 cubic centimeters (cm^3)
1 cubic decimeter	= 1000 cubic centimeters

Units of Capacity
1 kiloliter (kL)	= 1000 liters (L)
1 liter	= 1000 milliliters (mL)

Units of Mass
1 metric ton (t)	= 1000 kilograms (kg)
1 kilogram	= 1000 grams (g)
1 gram	= 1000 milligrams (mg)

Units of Time
1 century	= 100 years
1 decade	= 10 years
1 year (yr)	= 12 months
	= 52 weeks (plus one or two days)
	= 365 days (366 days in a leap year)
1 month (mo)	= 28, 29, 30, or 31 days
1 week (wk)	= 7 days
1 day (d)	= 24 hours
1 hour (hr)	= 60 minutes
1 minute (min)	= 60 seconds (sec)

U.S. Customary System

Units of Length
1 mile (mi)	= 1760 yards (yd)
	= 5280 feet (ft)
1 yard	= 3 feet
	= 36 inches (in.)
1 foot	= 12 inches

Units of Area
1 square yard (yd^2)	= 9 square feet (ft^2)
	= 1296 square inches ($in.^2$)
1 square foot	= 144 square inches
1 acre	= 43,560 square feet
1 square mile (mi^2)	= 640 acres

Units of Volume
1 cubic yard (yd^3)	= 27 cubic feet (ft^3)
1 cubic foot	= 1728 cubic inches ($in.^3$)

Units of Capacity
1 gallon (gal)	= 4 quarts (qt)
1 quart	= 2 pints (pt)
1 pint	= 2 cups (c)
1 cup	= 8 fluid ounces (fl oz)
1 fluid ounce	= 2 tablespoons (tbs)
1 tablespoon	= 3 teaspoons (tsp)

Units of Weight
1 ton (T)	= 2000 pounds (lb)
1 pound	= 16 ounces (oz)

System Equivalents

1 inch is about 2.5 cm (2.54)

1 kilometer is about 0.6 mile (0.621)

1 mile is about 1.6 kilometers (1.609)

1 meter is about 39 inches (39.37)

1 liter is about 1.1 quarts (1.057)

1 ounce is about 28 grams (28.350)

1 kilogram is about 2.2 pounds (2.205)

1 hectare is about 2.5 acres (2.47)

Rules for Order of Operations

1. Do operations within parentheses or other grouping symbols before doing anything else.
2. Calculate all powers.
3. Do multiplications or divisions in order, from left to right.
4. Then do additions or subtractions in order, from left to right.

Reference

Symbols

$+$	plus or positive
$-$	minus or negative
$*, \times$	multiplied by
$\div, /$	divided by
$=$	is equal to
$\neq$	is not equal to
$<$	is less than
$>$	is greater than
$\leq$	is less than or equal to
$\geq$	is greater than or equal to
x^n	nth power of x
$\sqrt{x}$	square root of x
$\%$	percent
$\frac{a}{b}, a{:}b, a/b$	ratio of a to b or a divided by b or the fraction $\frac{a}{b}$
$\circ$	degree
(a,b)	ordered pair
$\overleftrightarrow{AS}$	line AS
$\overline{AS}$	line segment AS
$\overrightarrow{AS}$	ray AS
$\llcorner$	right angle
$\perp$	is perpendicular to
$\parallel$	is parallel to
$\triangle ABC$	triangle ABC
$\angle ABC$	angle ABC
$\angle B$	angle B

Place-Value Chart

trillions	100B	10B	billions	100M	10M	millions	hundred-thousands	ten-thousands	thousands	hundreds	tens	ones	.	tenths	hundredths	thousandths
1000 billions			1000 millions			1,000,000s	100,000s	10,000s	1000s	100s	10s	1s	.	0.1s	0.01s	0.001s
10^{12}	10^{11}	10^{10}	10^{9}	10^{8}	10^{7}	10^{6}	10^{5}	10^{4}	10^{3}	10^{2}	10^{1}	10^{0}	.	10^{-1}	10^{-2}	10^{-3}

Probability Meter

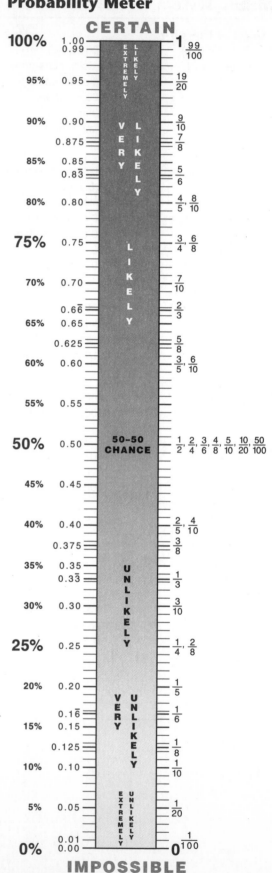

Reference

Latitude and Longitude

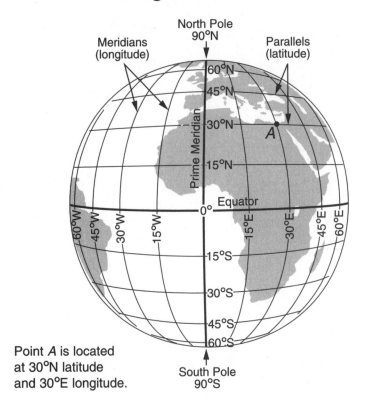

Point A is located at 30°N latitude and 30°E longitude.

Rational Numbers

Rule	Example
$\frac{a}{b} = \frac{n*a}{n*b}$	$\frac{2}{3} = \frac{4*2}{4*3} = \frac{8}{12}$
$\frac{a}{b} = \frac{a/n}{b/n}$	$\frac{8}{12} = \frac{8/4}{12/4} = \frac{2}{3}$
$\frac{a}{a} = a * \frac{1}{a} = 1$	$\frac{4}{4} = 4 * \frac{1}{4} = 1$
$\frac{a}{b} + \frac{c}{b} = \frac{a+c}{b}$	$\frac{3}{5} + \frac{1}{5} = \frac{3+1}{5} = \frac{4}{5}$
$\frac{a}{b} - \frac{c}{b} = \frac{a-c}{b}$	$\frac{3}{5} - \frac{1}{5} = \frac{3-1}{5} = \frac{2}{5}$
$\frac{a}{b} * \frac{c}{d} = \frac{a*c}{b*d}$	$\frac{1}{4} * \frac{2}{3} = \frac{1*2}{4*3} = \frac{2}{12}$

To compare, add, or subtract fractions:

1. Find a common denominator.

2. Rewrite fractions as equivalent fractions with the common denominator.

3. Compare, add, or subtract these fractions.

Fraction-Stick and Decimal Number-Line Chart

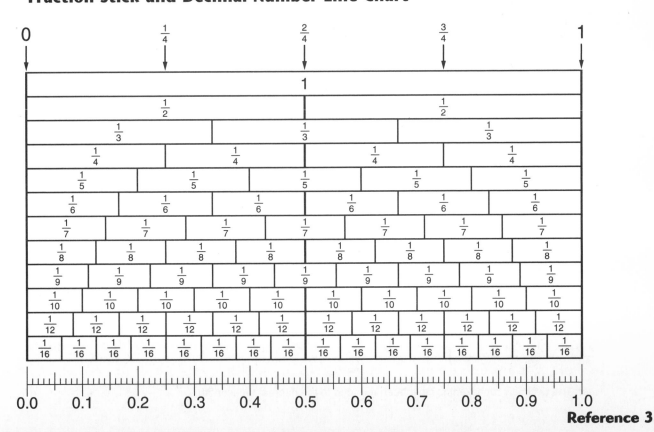

Reference

Equivalent Fractions, Decimals, and Percents

															Decimal	Percent
$\frac{1}{2}$	$\frac{2}{4}$	$\frac{3}{6}$	$\frac{4}{8}$	$\frac{5}{10}$	$\frac{6}{12}$	$\frac{7}{14}$	$\frac{8}{16}$	$\frac{9}{18}$	$\frac{10}{20}$	$\frac{11}{22}$	$\frac{12}{24}$	$\frac{13}{26}$	$\frac{14}{28}$	$\frac{15}{30}$	0.5	50%
$\frac{1}{3}$	$\frac{2}{6}$	$\frac{3}{9}$	$\frac{4}{12}$	$\frac{5}{15}$	$\frac{6}{18}$	$\frac{7}{21}$	$\frac{8}{24}$	$\frac{9}{27}$	$\frac{10}{30}$	$\frac{11}{33}$	$\frac{12}{36}$	$\frac{13}{39}$	$\frac{14}{42}$	$\frac{15}{45}$	$0.\overline{3}$	$33\frac{1}{3}\%$
$\frac{2}{3}$	$\frac{4}{6}$	$\frac{6}{9}$	$\frac{8}{12}$	$\frac{10}{15}$	$\frac{12}{18}$	$\frac{14}{21}$	$\frac{16}{24}$	$\frac{18}{27}$	$\frac{20}{30}$	$\frac{22}{33}$	$\frac{24}{36}$	$\frac{26}{39}$	$\frac{28}{42}$	$\frac{30}{45}$	$0.\overline{6}$	$66\frac{2}{3}\%$
$\frac{1}{4}$	$\frac{2}{8}$	$\frac{3}{12}$	$\frac{4}{16}$	$\frac{5}{20}$	$\frac{6}{24}$	$\frac{7}{28}$	$\frac{8}{32}$	$\frac{9}{36}$	$\frac{10}{40}$	$\frac{11}{44}$	$\frac{12}{48}$	$\frac{13}{52}$	$\frac{14}{56}$	$\frac{15}{60}$	0.25	25%
$\frac{3}{4}$	$\frac{6}{8}$	$\frac{9}{12}$	$\frac{12}{16}$	$\frac{15}{20}$	$\frac{18}{24}$	$\frac{21}{28}$	$\frac{24}{32}$	$\frac{27}{36}$	$\frac{30}{40}$	$\frac{33}{44}$	$\frac{36}{48}$	$\frac{39}{52}$	$\frac{42}{56}$	$\frac{45}{60}$	0.75	75%
$\frac{1}{5}$	$\frac{2}{10}$	$\frac{3}{15}$	$\frac{4}{20}$	$\frac{5}{25}$	$\frac{6}{30}$	$\frac{7}{35}$	$\frac{8}{40}$	$\frac{9}{45}$	$\frac{10}{50}$	$\frac{11}{55}$	$\frac{12}{60}$	$\frac{13}{65}$	$\frac{14}{70}$	$\frac{15}{75}$	0.2	20%
$\frac{2}{5}$	$\frac{4}{10}$	$\frac{6}{15}$	$\frac{8}{20}$	$\frac{10}{25}$	$\frac{12}{30}$	$\frac{14}{35}$	$\frac{16}{40}$	$\frac{18}{45}$	$\frac{20}{50}$	$\frac{22}{55}$	$\frac{24}{60}$	$\frac{26}{65}$	$\frac{28}{70}$	$\frac{30}{75}$	0.4	40%
$\frac{3}{5}$	$\frac{6}{10}$	$\frac{9}{15}$	$\frac{12}{20}$	$\frac{15}{25}$	$\frac{18}{30}$	$\frac{21}{35}$	$\frac{24}{40}$	$\frac{27}{45}$	$\frac{30}{50}$	$\frac{33}{55}$	$\frac{36}{60}$	$\frac{39}{65}$	$\frac{42}{70}$	$\frac{45}{75}$	0.6	60%
$\frac{4}{5}$	$\frac{8}{10}$	$\frac{12}{15}$	$\frac{16}{20}$	$\frac{20}{25}$	$\frac{24}{30}$	$\frac{28}{35}$	$\frac{32}{40}$	$\frac{36}{45}$	$\frac{40}{50}$	$\frac{44}{55}$	$\frac{48}{60}$	$\frac{52}{65}$	$\frac{56}{70}$	$\frac{60}{75}$	0.8	80%
$\frac{1}{6}$	$\frac{2}{12}$	$\frac{3}{18}$	$\frac{4}{24}$	$\frac{5}{30}$	$\frac{6}{36}$	$\frac{7}{42}$	$\frac{8}{48}$	$\frac{9}{54}$	$\frac{10}{60}$	$\frac{11}{66}$	$\frac{12}{72}$	$\frac{13}{78}$	$\frac{14}{84}$	$\frac{15}{90}$	$0.1\overline{6}$	$16\frac{2}{3}\%$
$\frac{5}{6}$	$\frac{10}{12}$	$\frac{15}{18}$	$\frac{20}{24}$	$\frac{25}{30}$	$\frac{30}{36}$	$\frac{35}{42}$	$\frac{40}{48}$	$\frac{45}{54}$	$\frac{50}{60}$	$\frac{55}{66}$	$\frac{60}{72}$	$\frac{65}{78}$	$\frac{70}{84}$	$\frac{75}{90}$	$0.8\overline{3}$	$83\frac{1}{3}\%$
$\frac{1}{7}$	$\frac{2}{14}$	$\frac{3}{21}$	$\frac{4}{28}$	$\frac{5}{35}$	$\frac{6}{42}$	$\frac{7}{49}$	$\frac{8}{56}$	$\frac{9}{63}$	$\frac{10}{70}$	$\frac{11}{77}$	$\frac{12}{84}$	$\frac{13}{91}$	$\frac{14}{98}$	$\frac{15}{105}$	0.143	14.3%
$\frac{2}{7}$	$\frac{4}{14}$	$\frac{6}{21}$	$\frac{8}{28}$	$\frac{10}{35}$	$\frac{12}{42}$	$\frac{14}{49}$	$\frac{16}{56}$	$\frac{18}{63}$	$\frac{20}{70}$	$\frac{22}{77}$	$\frac{24}{84}$	$\frac{26}{91}$	$\frac{28}{98}$	$\frac{30}{105}$	0.286	28.6%
$\frac{3}{7}$	$\frac{6}{14}$	$\frac{9}{21}$	$\frac{12}{28}$	$\frac{15}{35}$	$\frac{18}{42}$	$\frac{21}{49}$	$\frac{24}{56}$	$\frac{27}{63}$	$\frac{30}{70}$	$\frac{33}{77}$	$\frac{36}{84}$	$\frac{39}{91}$	$\frac{42}{98}$	$\frac{45}{105}$	0.429	42.9%
$\frac{4}{7}$	$\frac{8}{14}$	$\frac{12}{21}$	$\frac{16}{28}$	$\frac{20}{35}$	$\frac{24}{42}$	$\frac{28}{49}$	$\frac{32}{56}$	$\frac{36}{63}$	$\frac{40}{70}$	$\frac{44}{77}$	$\frac{48}{84}$	$\frac{52}{91}$	$\frac{56}{98}$	$\frac{60}{105}$	0.571	57.1%
$\frac{5}{7}$	$\frac{10}{14}$	$\frac{15}{21}$	$\frac{20}{28}$	$\frac{25}{35}$	$\frac{30}{42}$	$\frac{35}{49}$	$\frac{40}{56}$	$\frac{45}{63}$	$\frac{50}{70}$	$\frac{55}{77}$	$\frac{60}{84}$	$\frac{65}{91}$	$\frac{70}{98}$	$\frac{75}{105}$	0.714	71.4%
$\frac{6}{7}$	$\frac{12}{14}$	$\frac{18}{21}$	$\frac{24}{28}$	$\frac{30}{35}$	$\frac{36}{42}$	$\frac{42}{49}$	$\frac{48}{56}$	$\frac{54}{63}$	$\frac{60}{70}$	$\frac{66}{77}$	$\frac{72}{84}$	$\frac{78}{91}$	$\frac{84}{98}$	$\frac{90}{105}$	0.857	85.7%
$\frac{1}{8}$	$\frac{2}{16}$	$\frac{3}{24}$	$\frac{4}{32}$	$\frac{5}{40}$	$\frac{6}{48}$	$\frac{7}{56}$	$\frac{8}{64}$	$\frac{9}{72}$	$\frac{10}{80}$	$\frac{11}{88}$	$\frac{12}{96}$	$\frac{13}{104}$	$\frac{14}{112}$	$\frac{15}{120}$	0.125	$12\frac{1}{2}\%$
$\frac{3}{8}$	$\frac{6}{16}$	$\frac{9}{24}$	$\frac{12}{32}$	$\frac{15}{40}$	$\frac{18}{48}$	$\frac{21}{56}$	$\frac{24}{64}$	$\frac{27}{72}$	$\frac{30}{80}$	$\frac{33}{88}$	$\frac{36}{96}$	$\frac{39}{104}$	$\frac{42}{112}$	$\frac{45}{120}$	0.375	$37\frac{1}{2}\%$
$\frac{5}{8}$	$\frac{10}{16}$	$\frac{15}{24}$	$\frac{20}{32}$	$\frac{25}{40}$	$\frac{30}{48}$	$\frac{35}{56}$	$\frac{40}{64}$	$\frac{45}{72}$	$\frac{50}{80}$	$\frac{55}{88}$	$\frac{60}{96}$	$\frac{65}{104}$	$\frac{70}{112}$	$\frac{75}{120}$	0.625	$62\frac{1}{2}\%$
$\frac{7}{8}$	$\frac{14}{16}$	$\frac{21}{24}$	$\frac{28}{32}$	$\frac{35}{40}$	$\frac{42}{48}$	$\frac{49}{56}$	$\frac{56}{64}$	$\frac{63}{72}$	$\frac{70}{80}$	$\frac{77}{88}$	$\frac{84}{96}$	$\frac{91}{104}$	$\frac{98}{112}$	$\frac{105}{120}$	0.875	$87\frac{1}{2}\%$
$\frac{1}{9}$	$\frac{2}{18}$	$\frac{3}{27}$	$\frac{4}{36}$	$\frac{5}{45}$	$\frac{6}{54}$	$\frac{7}{63}$	$\frac{8}{72}$	$\frac{9}{81}$	$\frac{10}{90}$	$\frac{11}{99}$	$\frac{12}{108}$	$\frac{13}{117}$	$\frac{14}{126}$	$\frac{15}{135}$	$0.\overline{1}$	$11\frac{1}{9}\%$
$\frac{2}{9}$	$\frac{4}{18}$	$\frac{6}{27}$	$\frac{8}{36}$	$\frac{10}{45}$	$\frac{12}{54}$	$\frac{14}{63}$	$\frac{16}{72}$	$\frac{18}{81}$	$\frac{20}{90}$	$\frac{22}{99}$	$\frac{24}{108}$	$\frac{26}{117}$	$\frac{28}{126}$	$\frac{30}{135}$	$0.\overline{2}$	$22\frac{2}{9}\%$
$\frac{4}{9}$	$\frac{8}{18}$	$\frac{12}{27}$	$\frac{16}{36}$	$\frac{20}{45}$	$\frac{24}{54}$	$\frac{28}{63}$	$\frac{32}{72}$	$\frac{36}{81}$	$\frac{40}{90}$	$\frac{44}{99}$	$\frac{48}{108}$	$\frac{52}{117}$	$\frac{56}{126}$	$\frac{60}{135}$	$0.\overline{4}$	$44\frac{4}{9}\%$
$\frac{5}{9}$	$\frac{10}{18}$	$\frac{15}{27}$	$\frac{20}{36}$	$\frac{25}{45}$	$\frac{30}{54}$	$\frac{35}{63}$	$\frac{40}{72}$	$\frac{45}{81}$	$\frac{50}{90}$	$\frac{55}{99}$	$\frac{60}{108}$	$\frac{65}{117}$	$\frac{70}{126}$	$\frac{75}{135}$	$0.\overline{5}$	$55\frac{5}{9}\%$
$\frac{7}{9}$	$\frac{14}{18}$	$\frac{21}{27}$	$\frac{28}{36}$	$\frac{35}{45}$	$\frac{42}{54}$	$\frac{49}{63}$	$\frac{56}{72}$	$\frac{63}{81}$	$\frac{70}{90}$	$\frac{77}{99}$	$\frac{84}{108}$	$\frac{91}{117}$	$\frac{98}{126}$	$\frac{105}{135}$	$0.\overline{7}$	$77\frac{7}{9}\%$
$\frac{8}{9}$	$\frac{16}{18}$	$\frac{24}{27}$	$\frac{32}{36}$	$\frac{40}{45}$	$\frac{48}{54}$	$\frac{56}{63}$	$\frac{64}{72}$	$\frac{72}{81}$	$\frac{80}{90}$	$\frac{88}{99}$	$\frac{96}{108}$	$\frac{104}{117}$	$\frac{112}{126}$	$\frac{120}{135}$	$0.\overline{8}$	$88\frac{8}{9}\%$

Note: The decimals for sevenths have been rounded to the nearest thousandth.

Spoon Scramble Cards 1

$\frac{1}{7}$ of 42	$\frac{24}{4} * \frac{5}{5}$	$\frac{54}{9}$	$2\frac{16}{4}$
$\frac{1}{5}$ of 35	$\frac{21}{3} * \frac{4}{4}$	$\frac{56}{8}$	$4\frac{36}{12}$
$\frac{1}{8}$ of 64	$\frac{48}{6} * \frac{3}{3}$	$\frac{32}{4}$	$3\frac{25}{5}$
$\frac{1}{4}$ of 36	$\frac{63}{7} * \frac{6}{6}$	$\frac{72}{8}$	$5\frac{32}{8}$

Date

Time

Spoon Scramble Cards 2

$1 \div 2$	$\frac{35}{70}$	$\frac{1}{8} * 4$	0.5
$\frac{1}{3}$	$\frac{1}{6} * 2$	$33\frac{1}{3}\%$	$\frac{1}{2} - \frac{1}{6}$
$\frac{26}{13}$	$\left(\frac{6}{9} * \frac{9}{6}\right) * 2$	2	$4 * \frac{1}{2}$
$\frac{3}{4}$	$\frac{600}{800}$	0.75	$3 \div 4$

Use with Lesson 4.12.

Activity Sheet 2

First to 100 Problem Cards

How many inches are there in x feet? How many centimeters are there in x meters? 1	How many quarts are there in x gallons? 2	What is the smallest number of x's you can add to get a sum greater than 100? 3	Is $50 * x$ greater than 1,000? Is $\frac{x}{10}$ less than 1? 4
$\frac{1}{2}$ of $x = ?$ $\frac{1}{10}$ of $x = ?$ 5	$1 - x = ?$ $x + 998 = ?$ 6	If x people share 1,000 stamps equally, how many stamps will each person get? 7	What time will it be x minutes from now? What time was it x minutes ago? 8
It is 102 miles to your destination. You have gone x miles. How many miles are left? 9	What whole or mixed number equals x divided by 2? 10	Is x a prime or a composite number? Is x divisible by 2? 11	The time is 11:05 A.M. The train left x minutes ago. What time did the train leave? 12
Bill was born in 1939. Freddy was born the same day, but x years later. In what year was Freddy born? 13	Which is larger: $2 * x$ or $x + 50?$ 14	There are x rows of seats. There are 9 seats in each row. How many seats are there in all? 15	Sargon spent x cents on apples. If she paid with a \$5 bill, how much change should she get? 16

Activity Sheet 3

First to 100 Problem Cards (cont.)

The temperature was 25°F. It dropped x degrees. What is the new temperature? 17	Each story in a building is 10 feet high. If the building has x stories, how tall is it? 18	Which is larger: $2 * x$ or $\frac{100}{x}$? 19	$20 * x = ?$ 20
Name all of the whole-number factors of x. 21	Is x an even or an odd number? Is x divisible by 9? 22	Shalanda was born on a Tuesday. Linda was born x days later. On what day of the week was Linda born? 23	Will had a quarter plus x cents. How much money did he have in all? 24
Find the perimeter and area of this square. x cm x cm 25	What is the median of these weights? 5 pounds 21 pounds x pounds What is the range? 26	$x°$ $?°$ 27	$x^2 = ?$ 50% of $x^2 = ?$ 28
$(3x + 4) - 8 = ?$ 29	x out of 100 students voted for Ruby. Is this more than 25%, less than 25%, or exactly 25% of the students? 30	There are 200 students at Wilson School. x% speak Spanish. How many students speak Spanish? 31	People answered a survey question either Yes or No. x% answered Yes. What percent answered No? 32

Activity Sheet 4